1991
YEARBOOK of
ASTRONOMY

1991 YEARBOOK of ASTRONOMY

edited by

Patrick Moore

Sidgwick & Jackson Limited
LONDON

First Published in Great Britain 1990

Copyright © 1990 by Sidgwick and Jackson Limited

Published in Great Britain by
Sidgwick & Jackson Limited
1 Tavistock Chambers, Bloomsbury Way
London WC1A 2SG

0–283–06032 8 (hardback)
0–283–06033 6 (paperback)

Front cover:
False colour picture of the optical counterpart of the X-ray source
1E 111.9-3754: D. Maccagni, B. Garilli, I. M. Gioia, T. Maccacaro,
G. Vettolani and A. Wolter. The brightest galaxy in the cluster has been
nicknamed GREG (Giant-Red Envelope Galaxy). Reproduced by kind
permission of the European Southern Observatory.

Photoset by Rowland Phototypesetting Limited
Bury St Edmunds, Suffolk
Printed in Great Britain by
Butler and Tanner Ltd, Frome, Somerset

Contents

Editor's Foreword

There have been no major changes in pattern for our twenty-ninth *Yearbook*. Once again Gordon Taylor has provided all the lists of monthly phenomena, and we welcome again two of our most regular and valued contributors, Dr Paul Murdin of the Royal Greenwich Observatory and Dr David Allen of the Siding Spring Observatory in Australia. John Isles, known as one of the world's leading amateur observers of variable stars, has provided a major article as well as the usual lists of variables and maxima of Mira stars, while Robert Argyle has up-dated the list of double stars. Our historical article is written by Dr Allan Chapman of Oxford, and we welcome two newcomers to the *Yearbook* – not, we hope, for the last time – Professor A. P. Fairall of Cape Town and Dr Barry Welsh of the University of California.

Much attention has been paid to Austin's Comet, and we are delighted to have an account of it from Harold Ridley, one of our most senior and respected observers. A full survey of the Voyager 2 results from Neptune has been held over until the main analyses have been completed.

We hope that there is 'something for everybody': 1991 promises to be a fascinating year from an astronomical point of view.

PATRICK MOORE
Selsey, July 1990

7

Preface

New readers will find that all the information in this *Yearbook* is given in diagrammatic or descriptive form; the positions of the planets may easily be found on the specially designed star charts, while the monthly notes describe the movements of the planets and give details of other astronomical phenomena visible in both the northern and southern hemispheres. Two sets of the star charts are provided. The **Northern Charts** (pp. 14 to 39) are designed for use in latitude 52 degrees north, but may be used without alteration throughout the British Isles, and (except in the case of eclipses and occultations) in other countries of similar north latitude. The **Southern Charts** (pp. 40 to 65) are drawn for latitude 35 degrees south, and are suitable for use in South Africa, Australia and New Zealand, and other stations in approximately the same south latitude. The reader who needs more detailed information will find *Norton's Star Atlas* (Longman) an invaluable guide, while more precise positions of the planets and their satellites, together with predictions of occultations, meteor showers, and periodic comets may be found in the *Handbook* of the British Astronomical Association. The British monthly periodical, with current news, articles, and monthly notes is *Astronomy Now*. Readers will also find details of forthcoming events given in the American *Sky and Telescope*. This monthly publication also produces a special occultation supplement giving predictions for the United States and Canada.

Important Note
The times given on the star charts and in the Monthly Notes are generally given as local times, using the 24-hour clock, the day beginning at midnight. All the dates, and the times of a few events (e.g. eclipses), are given in Greenwich Mean Time (G.M.T.), which is related to local time by the formula

Local Mean Time = G.M.T. − west longitude

In practice, small differences of longitudes are ignored, and the observer will use local clock time, which will be the appropriate

Standard (or Zone) Time. As the formula indicates, places in west longitude will have a Standard Time slow on G.M.T., while places in east longitude will have a Standard Time fast on G.M.T. As examples we have:

Standard Time in

New Zealand	G.M.T.	+	12 hours
Victoria; N.S.W.	G.M.T.	+	10 hours
Western Australia	G.M.T.	+	8 hours
South Africa	G.M.T.	+	2 hours
British Isles	G.M.T.		
Eastern S.T.	G.M.T.	−	5 hours
Central S.T.	G.M.T.	−	6 hours, etc.

If Summer Time is in use, the clocks will have to have been advanced by one hour, and this hour must be subtracted from the clock time to give Standard Time.

In Great Britain and N. Ireland, Summer Time will be in force in 1991 from March 31^{d}01^h until October 27^{d}01^h G.M.T.

Notes on the Star Charts

The stars, together with the Sun, Moon and planets seem to be set on the surface of the celestial sphere, which appears to rotate about the Earth from east to west. Since it is impossible to represent a curved surface accurately on a plane, any kind of star map is bound to contain some form of distortion. But it is well known that the eye can endure some kinds of distortion better than others, and it is particularly true that the eye is most sensitive to deviations from the vertical and horizontal. For this reason the star charts given in this volume have been designed to give a true representation of vertical and horizontal lines, whatever may be the resulting distortion in the shape of a constellation figure. It will be found that the amount of distortion is, in general, quite small, and is only obvious in the case of large constellations such as Leo and Pegasus, when these appear at the top of the charts, and so are drawn out sideways.

The charts show all stars down to the fourth magnitude, together with a number of fainter stars which are necessary to define the shape of a constellation. There is no standard system for representing the outlines of the constellations, and triangles and other simple figures have been used to give outlines which are easy to follow with the naked eye. The names of the constellations are given, together with the proper names of the brighter stars. The apparent magnitudes of the stars are indicated roughly by using four different sizes of dots, the larger dots representing the brighter stars.

The two sets of star charts are similar in design. At each opening there is a group of four charts which give a complete coverage of the sky up to an altitude of 62½ degrees; there are twelve such groups to cover the entire year. In the **Northern Charts** (for 52 degrees north) the upper two charts show the southern sky, south being at the centre and east on the left. The coverage is from 10 degrees north of east (top left) to 10 degrees north of west (top right). The two lower charts show the northern sky from 10 degrees south of west (lower left) to 10 degrees south of east (lower right). There is thus an overlap east and west.

Conversely, in the **Southern Charts** (for 35 degrees south) the upper two charts show the northern sky, with north at the centre and east on the right. The two lower charts show the southern sky, with south at the centre and east on the left. The coverage and overlap is the same on both sets of charts.

Because the sidereal day is shorter than the solar day, the stars appear to rise and set about four minutes earlier each day, and this amounts to two hours in a month. Hence the twelve groups of charts in each set are sufficient to give the appearance of the sky throughout the day at intervals of two hours, or at the same time of night at monthly intervals throughout the year. The actual range of dates and times when the stars on the charts are visible is indicated at the top of each page. Each group is numbered in bold type, and the number to be used for any given month and time is summarized in the following table:

Local Time	18h	20h	22h	0h	2h	4h	6h
January	11	12	1	2	3	4	5
February	12	1	2	3	4	5	6
March	1	2	3	4	5	6	7
April	2	3	4	5	6	7	8
May	3	4	5	6	7	8	9
June	4	5	6	7	8	9	10
July	5	6	7	8	9	10	11
August	6	7	8	9	10	11	12
September	7	8	9	10	11	12	1
October	8	9	10	11	12	1	2
November	9	10	11	12	1	2	3
December	10	11	12	1	2	3	4

The charts are drawn to scale, the horizontal measurements, marked at every 10 degrees, giving the azimuths (or true bearings) measured from the north round through east (90 degrees), south (180 degrees), and west (270 degrees). The vertical measurements, similarly marked, give the altitudes of the stars up to 62½ degrees. Estimates of altitude and azimuth made from these charts will necessarily be mere approximations, since no observer will be exactly at the adopted latitude, or at the stated time, but they will serve for the identification of stars and planets.

The ecliptic is drawn as a broken line on which longitude is marked at every 10 degrees; the positions of the planets are then easily found by reference to the table on page 71. It will be noticed that on the Southern Charts the **ecliptic** may reach an altitude in excess of 62½ degrees on star charts 5 to 9. The continuations of the broken line will be found on the charts of overhead stars.

There is a curious illusion that stars at an altitude of 60 degrees or more are actually overhead, and the beginner may often feel that he is leaning over backwards in trying to see them. These overhead stars are given separately on the pages immediately following the main star charts. The entire year is covered at one opening, each of the four maps showing the overhead stars at times which correspond to those of three of the main star charts. The position of the zenith is indicated by a cross, and this cross marks the centre of a circle which is 35 degrees from the zenith; there is thus a small overlap with the main charts.

The broken line leading from the north (on the Northern Charts) or from the south (on the Southern Charts) is numbered to indicate the corresponding main chart. Thus on page 38 the N-S line numbered 6 is to be regarded as an extension of the centre (south) line of chart 6 on pages 24 and 25, and at the top of these pages are printed the dates and times which are appropriate. Similarly, on page 65, the S-N line numbered 10 connects with the north line of the upper charts on pages 58 and 59.

The overhead stars are plotted as maps on a conical projection, and the scale is rather smaller than that of the main charts.

1L

October 6 at 5ʰ   October 21 at   4ʰ
November 6 at 3ʰ   November 21 at   2ʰ
December 6 at 1ʰ   December 21 at midnight
January 6 at 23ʰ   January 21 at   22ʰ
February 6 at 21ʰ   February 21 at   20ʰ

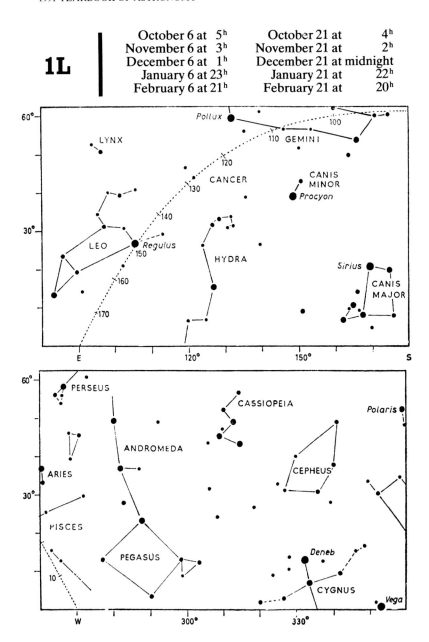

October 6 at 5ʰ   October 21 at 4ʰ
November 6 at 3ʰ   November 21 at 2ʰ
December 6 at 1ʰ   December 21 at midnight
January 6 at 23ʰ   January 21 at 22ʰ
February 6 at 21ʰ   February 21 at 20ʰ

1R

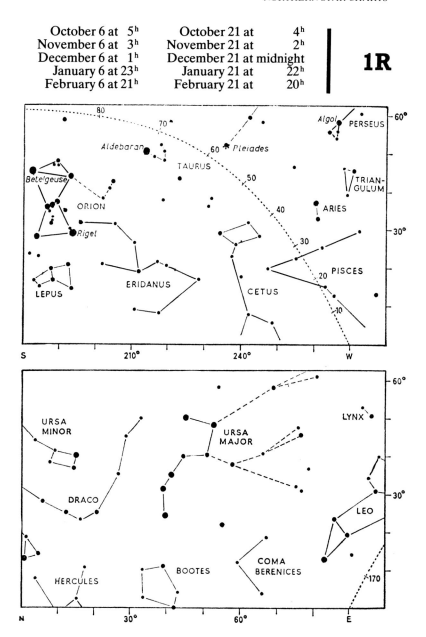

2L

November 6 at 5^h	November 21 at 4^h
December 6 at 3^h	December 21 at 2^h
January 6 at 1^h	January 21 at midnight
February 6 at 23^h	February 21 at 22^h
March 6 at 21^h	March 21 at 20^h

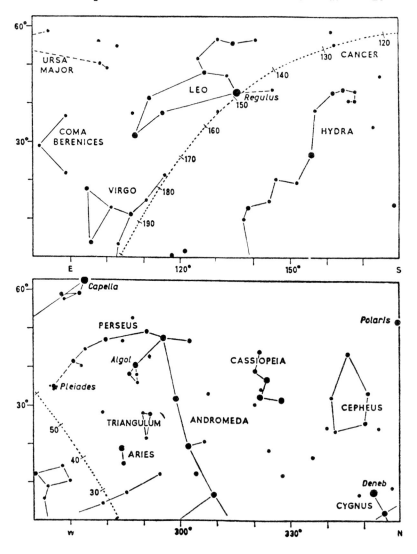

November 6 at 5ʰ	November 21 at 4ʰ	
December 6 at 3ʰ	December 21 at 2ʰ	
January 6 at 1ʰ	January 21 at midnight	**2R**
February 6 at 23ʰ	February 21 at 22ʰ	
March 6 at 21ʰ	March 21 at 20ʰ	

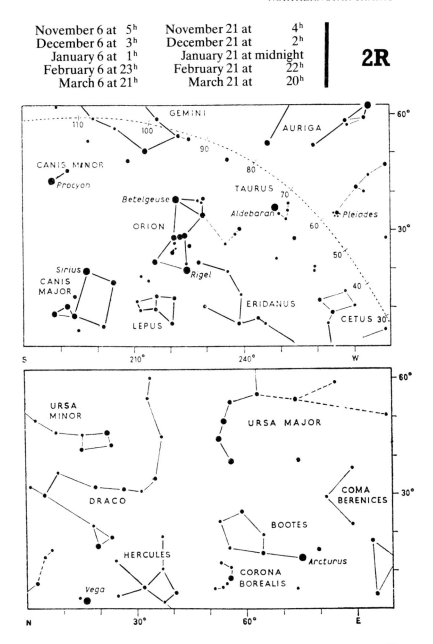

17

3L

December 6 at 5^h December 21 at 4^h
January 6 at 3^h January 21 at 2^h
February 6 at 1^h February 21 at midnight
March 6 at 23^h March 21 at 22^h
April 6 at 21^h April 21 at 20^h

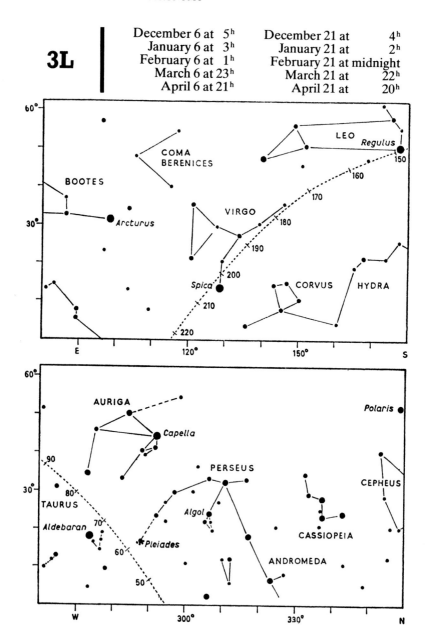

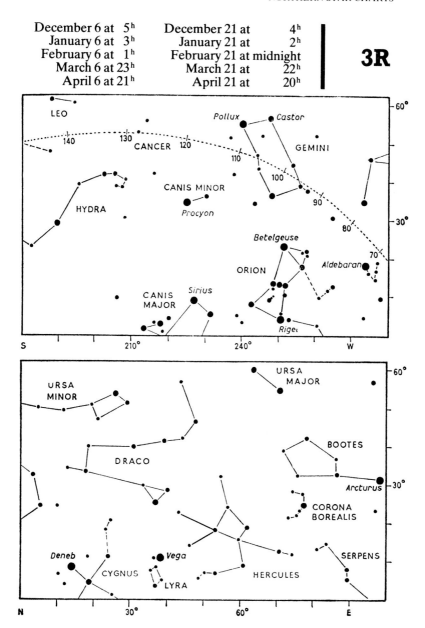

December 6 at 5ʰ   December 21 at   4ʰ
January 6 at 3ʰ   January 21 at   2ʰ
February 6 at 1ʰ   February 21 at midnight
March 6 at 23ʰ   March 21 at   22ʰ
April 6 at 21ʰ   April 21 at   20ʰ

3R

LEO

Pollux   Castor

140   130   120   110   100   90   80   70

CANCER

GEMINI

CANIS MINOR

HYDRA

Procyon

Betelgeuse

Aldebaran

ORION

CANIS   Sirius
MAJOR

Rigel

S   210°   240°   W

URSA
MINOR

URSA
MAJOR

BOOTES

DRACO

Arcturus

CORONA
BOREALIS

Deneb   Vega

SERPENS

CYGNUS

HERCULES

LYRA

N   30°   60°   E

19

4L

January 6 at 5^h	January 21 at 4^h
February 6 at 3^h	February 21 at 2^h
March 6 at 1^h	March 21 at midnight
April 6 at 23^h	April 21 at 22^h
May 6 at 21^h	May 21 at 20^h

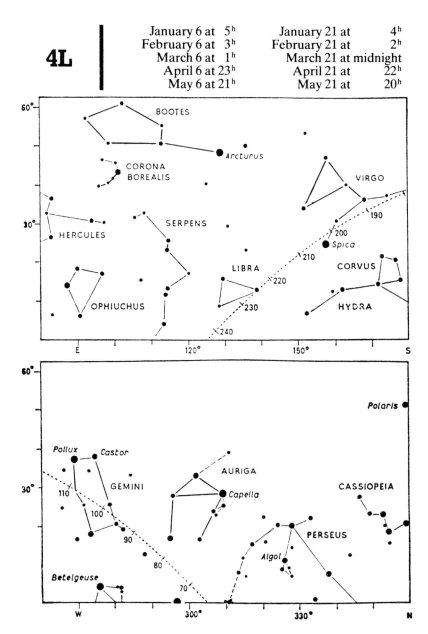

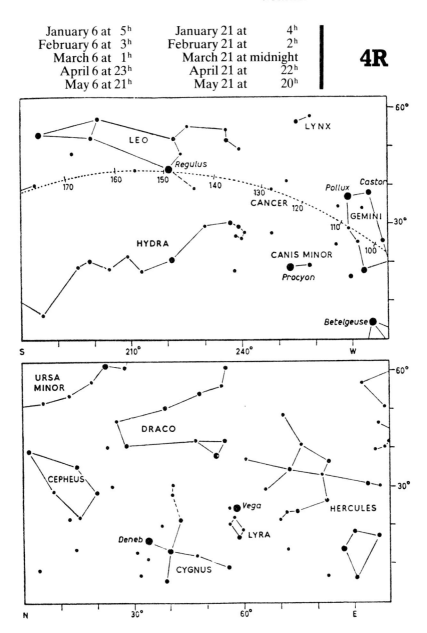

January 6 at 5^h January 21 at   4^h
February 6 at 3^h February 21 at   2^h
March 6 at 1^h March 21 at midnight
April 6 at 23^h April 21 at   22^h
May 6 at 21^h May 21 at   20^h

4R

LYNX

LEO

Regulus

170   160   150   140

130   CANCER   120

Pollux   Castor

GEMINI

HYDRA

CANIS MINOR

Procyon

110

100

60°

30°

Betelgeuse

S   210°   240°   W

URSA
MINOR

60°

DRACO

CEPHEUS

30°

Vega

HERCULES

Deneb

LYRA

CYGNUS

N   30°   60°   E

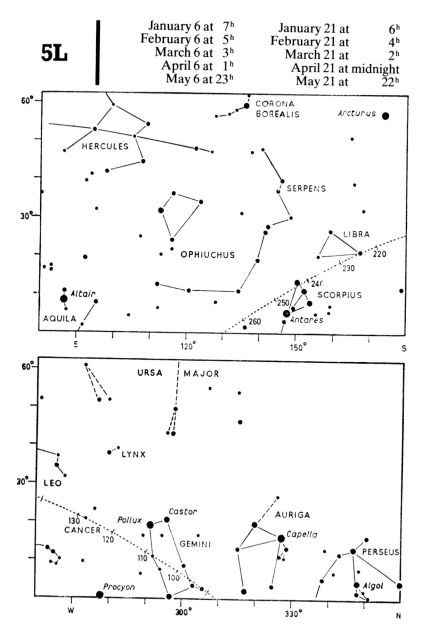

5L

January 6 at 7ʰ January 21 at 6ʰ
February 6 at 5ʰ February 21 at 4ʰ
March 6 at 3ʰ March 21 at 2ʰ
April 6 at 1ʰ April 21 at midnight
May 6 at 23ʰ May 21 at 22ʰ

January 6 at 7ʰ   January 21 at   6ʰ
February 6 at 5ʰ   February 21 at   4ʰ
March 6 at 3ʰ   March 21 at   2ʰ   **5R**
April 6 at 1ʰ   April 21 at midnight
May 6 at 23ʰ   May 21 at   22ʰ

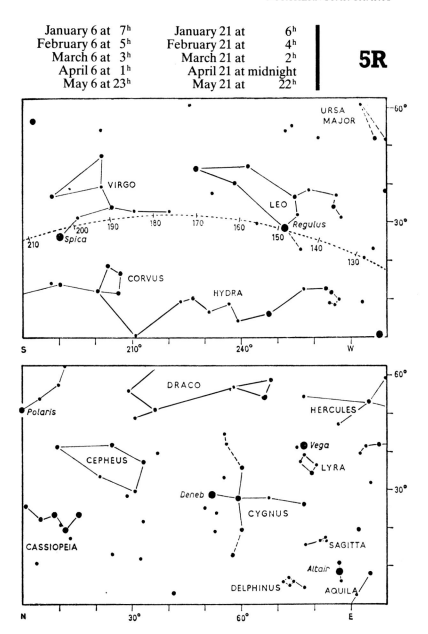

6L

March 6 at 5^h	March 21 at 4^h
April 6 at 3^h	April 21 at 2^h
May 6 at 1^h	May 21 at midnight
June 6 at 23^h	June 21 at 22^h
July 6 at 21^h	July 21 at 20^h

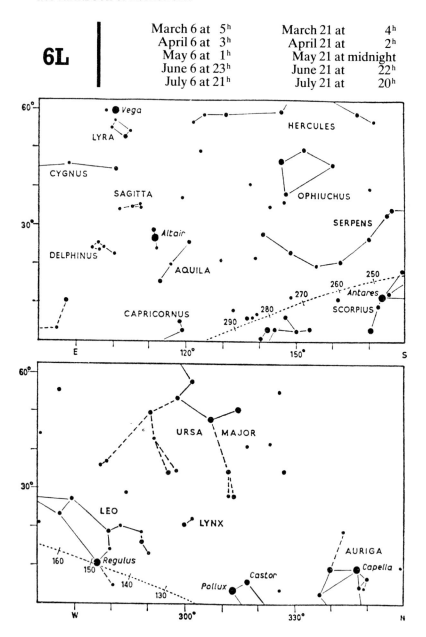

March 6 at 5ʰ   March 21 at   4ʰ
April 6 at 3ʰ   April 21 at   2ʰ
May 6 at 1ʰ   May 21 at midnight
June 6 at 23ʰ   June 21 at   22ʰ
July 6 at 21ʰ   July 21 at   20ʰ

6R

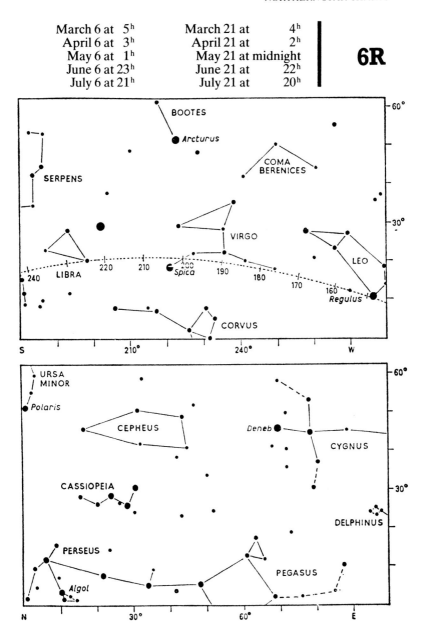

7L

May 6 at 3ʰ	May 21 at 2ʰ
June 6 at 1ʰ	June 21 at midnight
July 6 at 23ʰ	July 21 at 22ʰ
August 6 at 21ʰ	August 21 at 20ʰ
September 6 at 19ʰ	September 21 at 18ʰ

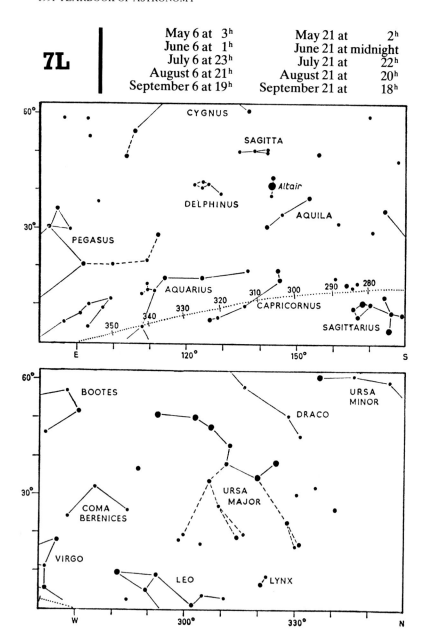

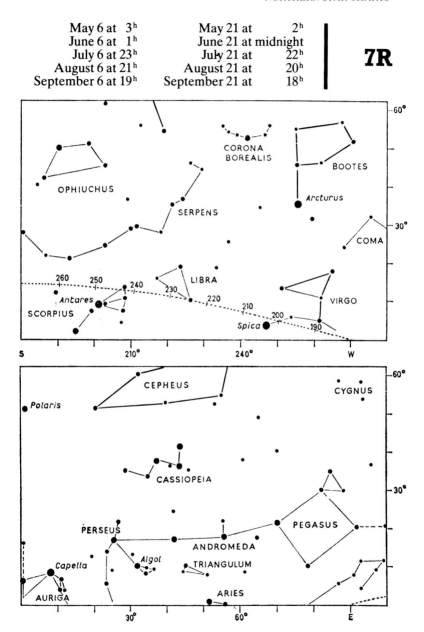

May 6 at	3ʰ	May 21 at	2ʰ
June 6 at	1ʰ	June 21 at midnight	
July 6 at	23ʰ	July 21 at	22ʰ
August 6 at	21ʰ	August 21 at	20ʰ
September 6 at	19ʰ	September 21 at	18ʰ

7R

8L

July 6 at 1ʰ	July 21 at midnight
August 6 at 23ʰ	August 21 at 22ʰ
September 6 at 21ʰ	September 21 at 20ʰ
October 6 at 19ʰ	October 21 at 18ʰ
November 6 at 17ʰ	November 21 at 16ʰ

July 6 at 1ʰ	July 21 at midnight	
August 6 at 23ʰ	August 21 at	22ʰ
September 6 at 21ʰ	September 21 at	20ʰ
October 6 at 19ʰ	October 21 at	18ʰ
November 6 at 17ʰ	November 21 at	16ʰ

8R

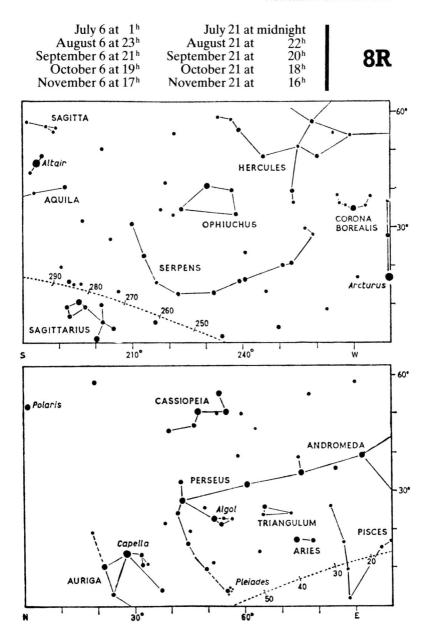

9L

August 6 at 1ʰ	August 21 at midnight
September 6 at 23ʰ	September 21 at 22ʰ
October 6 at 21ʰ	October 21 at 20ʰ
November 6 at 19ʰ	November 21 at 18ʰ
December 6 at 17ʰ	December 21 at 16ʰ

August 6 at 1^h	August 21 at midnight	
September 6 at 23^h	September 21 at 22^h	
October 6 at 21^h	October 21 at 20^h	**9R**
November 6 at 19^h	November 21 at 18^h	
December 6 at 17^h	December 21 at 16^h	

10L

August 6 at 3^h	August 21 at 2^h
September 6 at 1^h	September 21 at midnight
October 6 at 23^h	October 21 at 22^h
November 6 at 21^h	November 21 at 20^h
December 6 at 19^h	December 21 at 18^h

August 6 at 3ʰ   August 21 at 2ʰ
September 6 at 1ʰ   September 21 at midnight
October 6 at 23ʰ   October 21 at 22ʰ
November 6 at 21ʰ   November 21 at 20ʰ
December 6 at 19ʰ   December 21 at 18ʰ

10R

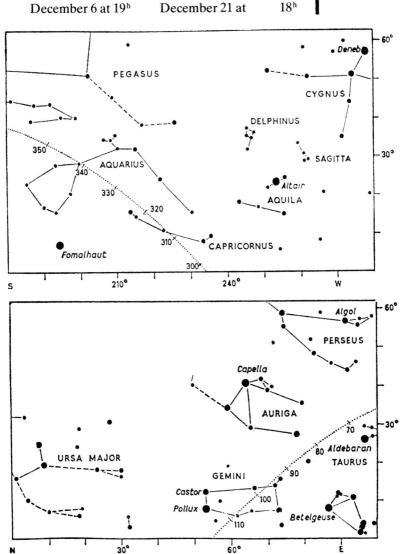

11L

September 6 at 3ʰ
October 6 at 1ʰ
November 6 at 23ʰ
December 6 at 21ʰ
January 6 at 19ʰ

September 21 at 2ʰ
October 21 at midnight
November 21 at 22ʰ
December 21 at 20ʰ
January 21 at 18ʰ

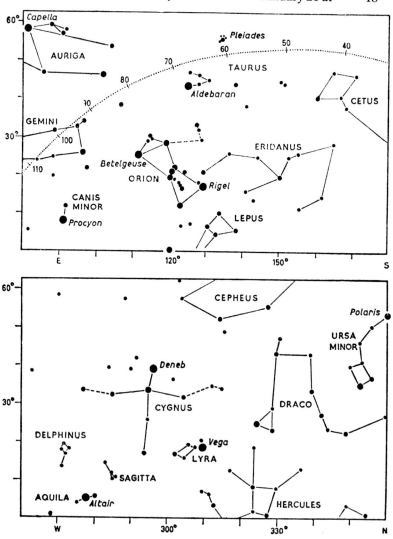

September 6 at 3ʰ   September 21 at 2ʰ
October 6 at 1ʰ   October 21 at midnight
November 6 at 23ʰ   November 21 at 22ʰ
December 6 at 21ʰ   December 21 at 20ʰ
January 6 at 19ʰ   January 21 at 18ʰ

11R

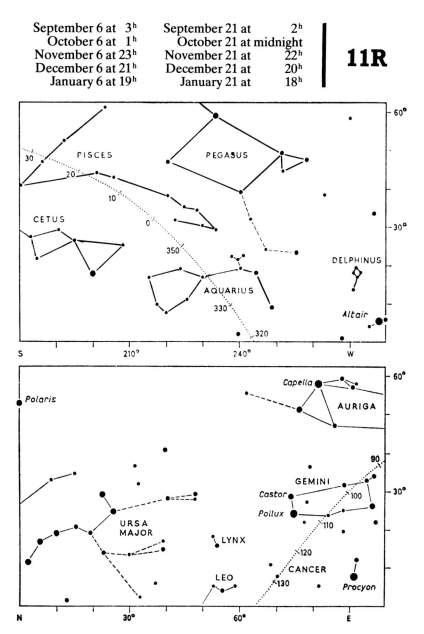

12L

October 6 at 3^h	October 21 at 2^h
November 6 at 1^h	November 21 at midnight
December 6 at 23^h	December 21 at 22^h
January 6 at 21^h	January 21 at 20^h
February 6 at 19^h	February 21 at 18^h

October 6 at 3ʰ	October 21 at 2ʰ	
November 6 at 1ʰ	November 21 at midnight	
December 6 at 23ʰ	December 21 at 22ʰ	**12R**
January 6 at 21ʰ	January 21 at 20ʰ	
February 6 at 19ʰ	February 21 at 18ʰ	

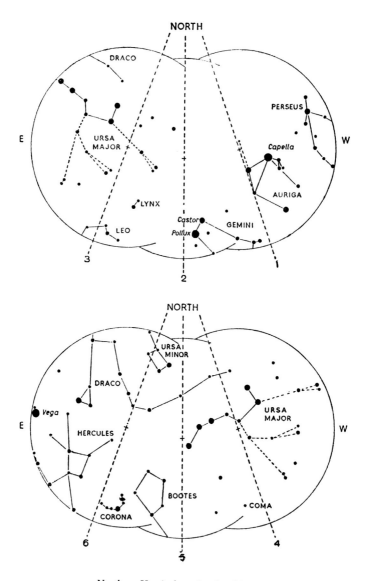

Northern Hemisphere Overhead Stars

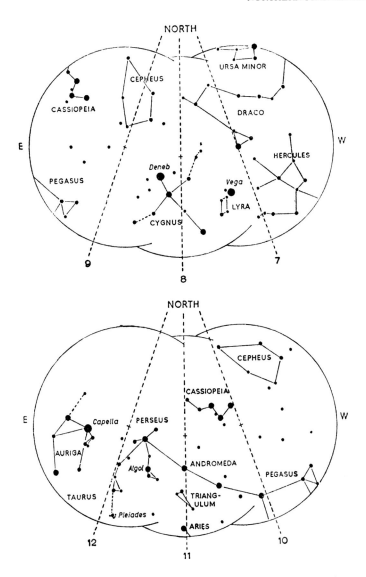

Northern Hemisphere Overhead Stars

1L

October 6 at 5^h	October 21 at 4^h
November 6 at 3^h	November 21 at 2^h
December 6 at 1^h	December 21 at midnight
January 6 at 23^h	January 21 at 22^h
February 6 at 21^h	February 21 at 20^h

October 6 at 5ʰ   October 21 at 4ʰ
November 6 at 3ʰ   November 21 at 2ʰ
December 6 at 1ʰ   December 21 at midnight
January 6 at 23ʰ   January 21 at 22ʰ
February 6 at 21ʰ   February 21 at 20ʰ

1R

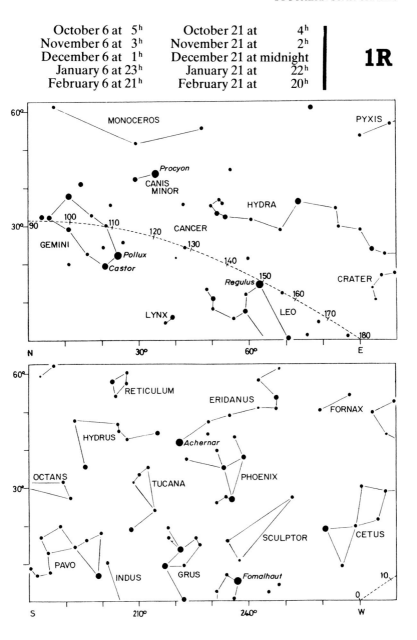

2L

November 6 at 5^h	November 21 at 4^h
December 6 at 3^h	December 21 at 2^h
January 6 at 1^h	January 21 at midnight
February 6 at 23^h	February 21 at 22^h
March 6 at 21^h	March 21 at 20^h

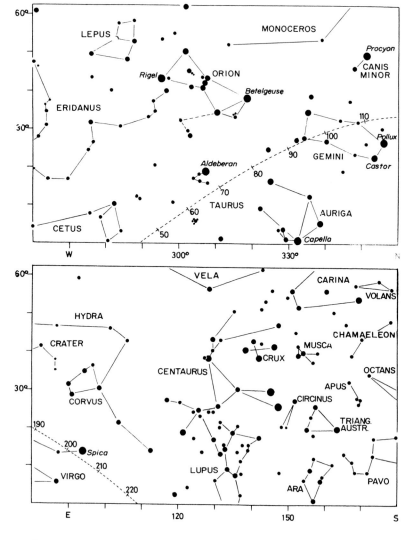

November 6 at   5^h November 21 at   4^h
December 6 at   3^h December 21 at   2^h
January 6 at   1^h January 21 at midnight
February 6 at 23^h February 21 at   22^h
March 6 at 21^h March 21 at   20^h

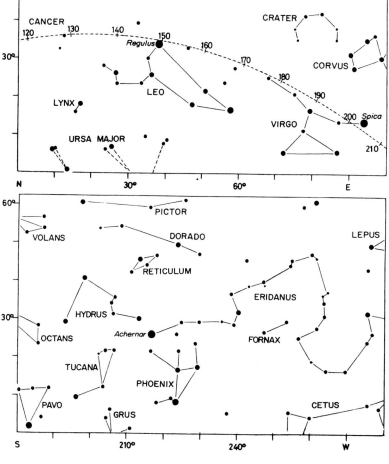

3L

January 6 at 3ʰ	January 21 at 2ʰ
February 6 at 1ʰ	February 21 at midnight
March 6 at 23ʰ	March 21 at 22ʰ
April 6 at 21ʰ	April 21 at 20ʰ
May 6 at 19ʰ	May 21 at 18ʰ

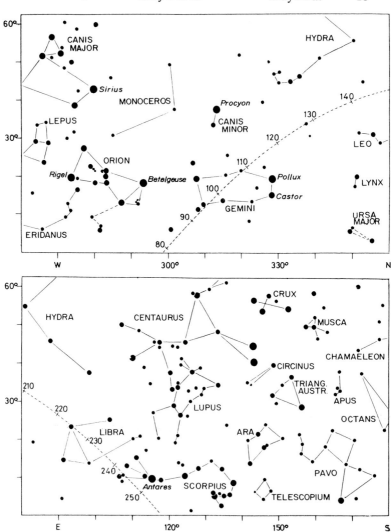

January 6 at 3ʰ   January 21 at   2ʰ
February 6 at 1ʰ   February 21 at midnight
March 6 at 23ʰ   March 21 at   22ʰ
April 6 at 21ʰ   April 21 at   20ʰ
May 6 at 19ʰ   May 21 at   18ʰ

3R

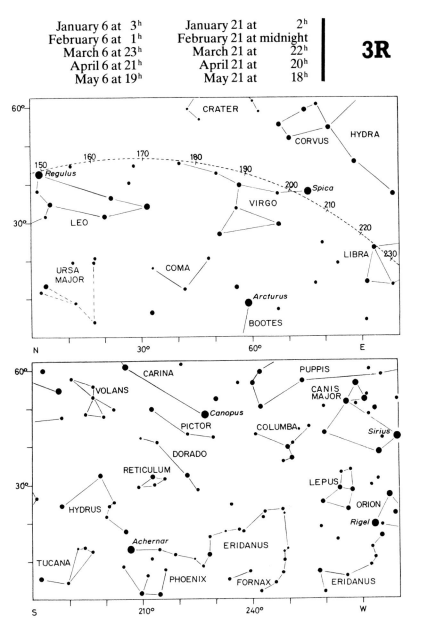

4L

February 6 at 3ʰ	February 21 at 2ʰ
March 6 at 1ʰ	March 21 at midnight
April 6 at 23ʰ	April 21 at 22ʰ
May 6 at 21ʰ	May 21 at 20ʰ
June 6 at 19ʰ	June 21 at 18ʰ

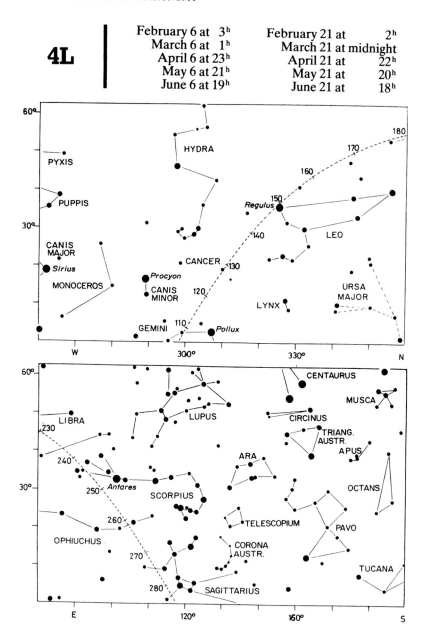

February 6 at 3ʰ	February 21 at 2ʰ	
March 6 at 1ʰ	March 21 at midnight	**4R**
April 6 at 23ʰ	April 21 at 22ʰ	
May 6 at 21ʰ	May 21 at 20ʰ	
June 6 at 19ʰ	June 21 at 18ʰ	

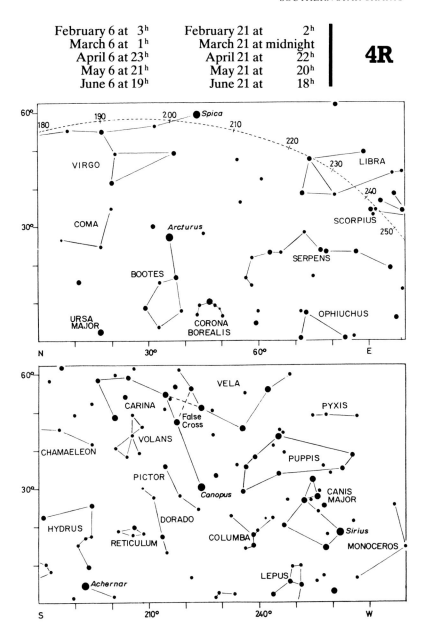

5L

March 6 at 3ʰ	March 21 at 2ʰ
April 6 at 1ʰ	April 21 at midnight
May 6 at 23ʰ	May 21 at 22ʰ
June 6 at 21ʰ	June 21 at 20ʰ
July 6 at 19ʰ	July 21 at 18ʰ

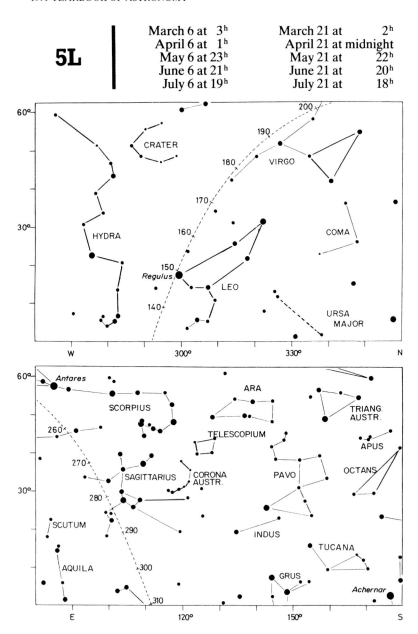

March 6 at 3ʰ   March 21 at   2ʰ
April 6 at 1ʰ   April 21 at midnight
May 6 at 23ʰ   May 21 at   22ʰ
June 6 at 21ʰ   June 21 at   20ʰ
July 6 at 19ʰ   July 21 at   18ʰ

5R

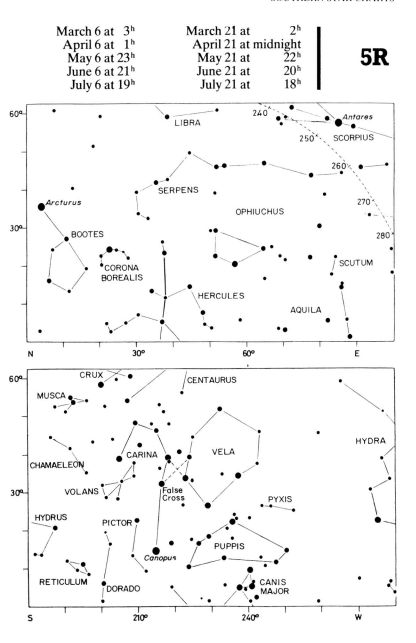

6L

March 6 at 5^h	March 21 at 4^h
April 6 at 3^h	April 21 at 2^h
May 6 at 1^h	May 21 at midnight
June 6 at 23^h	June 21 at 22^h
July 6 at 21^h	July 21 at 20^h

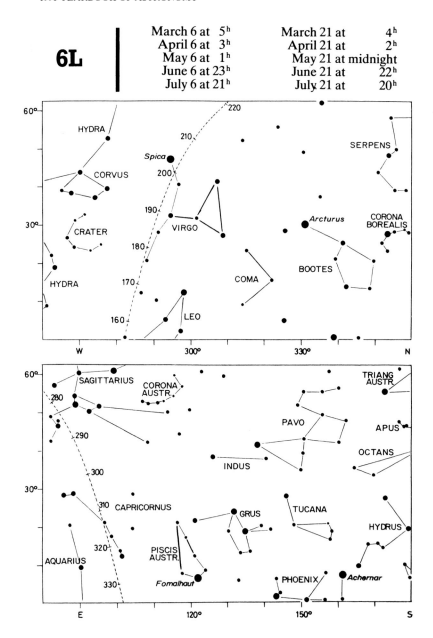

March 6 at 5ʰ	March 21 at 4ʰ
April 6 at 3ʰ	April 21 at 2ʰ
May 6 at 1ʰ	May 21 at midnight
June 6 at 23ʰ	June 21 at 22ʰ
July 6 at 21ʰ	July 21 at 20ʰ

6R

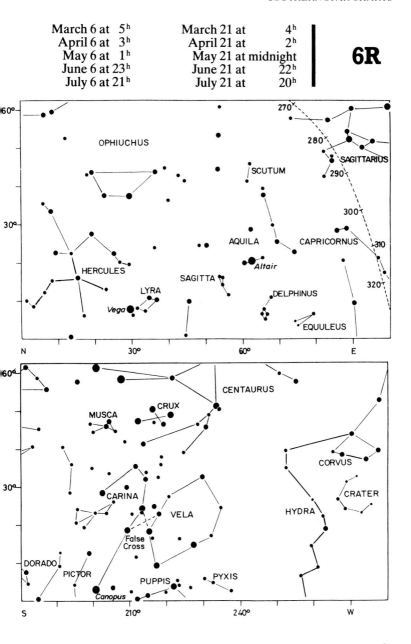

7L

April 6 at 5ʰ
May 6 at 3ʰ
June 6 at 1ʰ
July 6 at 23ʰ
August 6 at 21ʰ

April 21 at 4ʰ
May 21 at 2ʰ
June 21 at midnight
July 21 at 22ʰ
August 21 at 20ʰ

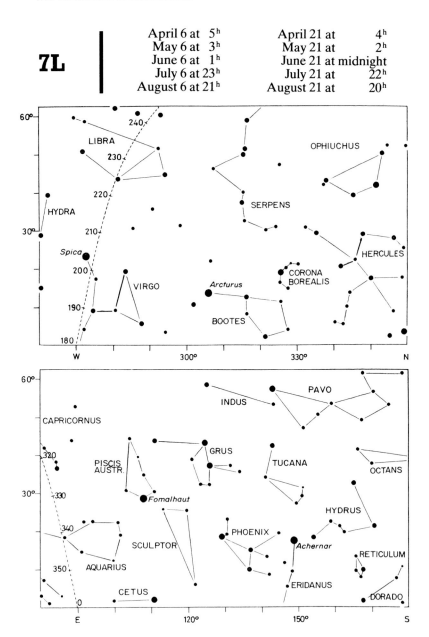

April 6 at 5ʰ   April 21 at 4ʰ
May 6 at 3ʰ   May 21 at 2ʰ
June 6 at 1ʰ   June 21 at midnight
July 6 at 23ʰ   July 21 at 22ʰ
August 6 at 21ʰ   August 21 at 20ʰ

7R

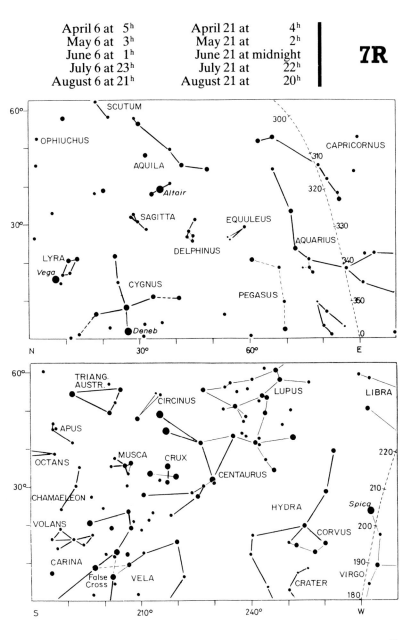

8L

May 6 at 5^h	May 21 at 4^h
June 6 at 3^h	June 21 at 2^h
July 6 at 1^h	July 21 at midnight
August 6 at 23^h	August 21 at 22^h
September 6 at 21^h	September 21 at 20^h

May 6 at 5ʰ	May 21 at 4ʰ	
June 6 at 3ʰ	June 21 at 2ʰ	**8R**
July 6 at 1ʰ	July 21 at midnight	
August 6 at 23ʰ	August 21 at 22ʰ	
September 6 at 21ʰ	September 21 at 20ʰ	

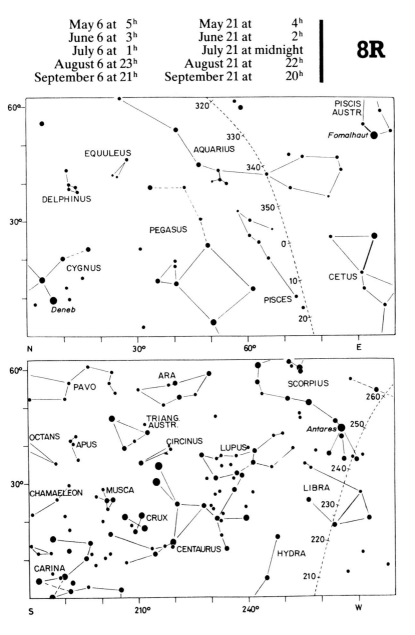

9L

June 6 at 5ʰ	June 21 at 4ʰ
July 6 at 3ʰ	July 21 at 2ʰ
August 6 at 1ʰ	August 21 at midnight
September 6 at 23ʰ	September 21 at 22ʰ
October 6 at 21ʰ	October 21 at 20ʰ

June 6 at   5ʰ   June 21 at   4ʰ
July 6 at   3ʰ   July 21 at   2ʰ
August 6 at 1ʰ   August 21 at midnight
September 6 at 23ʰ   September 21 at   22ʰ
October 6 at 21ʰ   October 21 at   20ʰ

9R

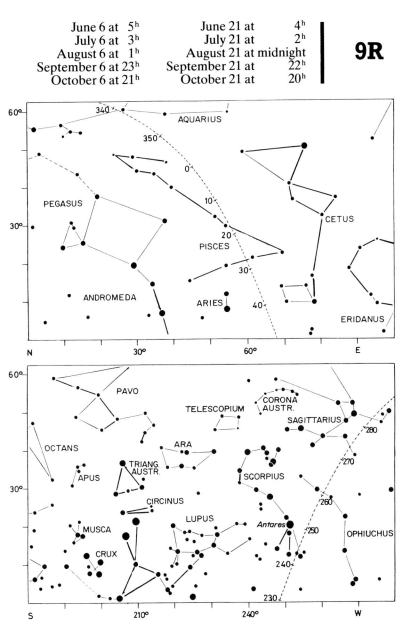

10L

July 6 at 5^h
August 6 at 3^h
September 6 at 1^h
October 6 at 23^h
November 6 at 21^h

July 21 at 4^h
August 21 at 2^h
September 21 at midnight
October 21 at 22^h
November 21 at 20^h

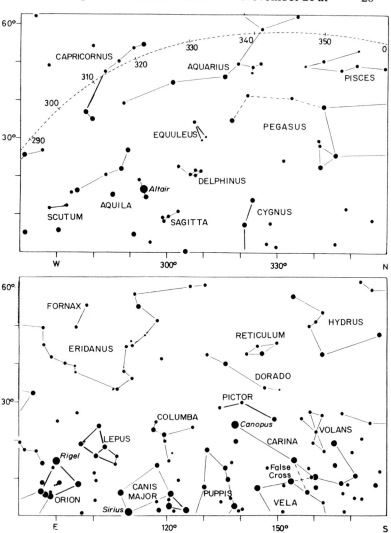

July 6 at 5ʰ	July 21 at	4ʰ
August 6 at 3ʰ	August 21 at	2ʰ
September 6 at 1ʰ	September 21 at midnight	
October 6 at 23ʰ	October 21 at	22ʰ
November 6 at 21ʰ	November 21 at	20ʰ

10R

CETUS

FORNAX

0

10

20

30

PISCES

40

ERIDANUS

30°

ARIES

50

TRIANGULUM

TAURUS

60

ANDROMEDA

Pleiades

Rigel

PERSEUS

Aldebaran

Algol

ORION

N   30°   60°   E

60°

INDUS

310

PAVO

300

OCTANS

TELESCOPIUM

290

APUS

CORONA.
AUSTR.

30°

TRIANG.
AUSTR

ARA

280

SAGITTARIUS

MUSCA

CIRCINUS

270

CRUX

SCORPIUS

SCUTUM

LUPUS

260

OPHIUCHUS

S   210°   240°   W

59

11L

August 6 at 5ʰ	August 21 at 4ʰ
September 6 at 3ʰ	September 21 at 2ʰ
October 6 at 1ʰ	October 21 at midnight
November 6 at 23ʰ	November 21 at 22ʰ
December 6 at 21ʰ	December 21 at 20ʰ

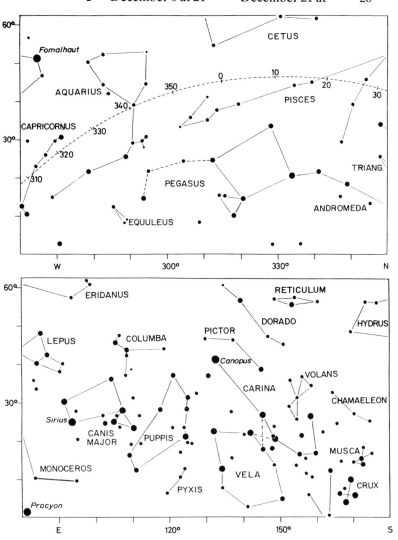

August 6 at 5^h	August 21 at 4^h	
September 6 at 3^h	September 21 at 2^h	**11R**
October 6 at 1^h	October 21 at midnight	
November 6 at 23^h	November 21 at 22^h	
December 6 at 21^h	December 21 at 20^h	

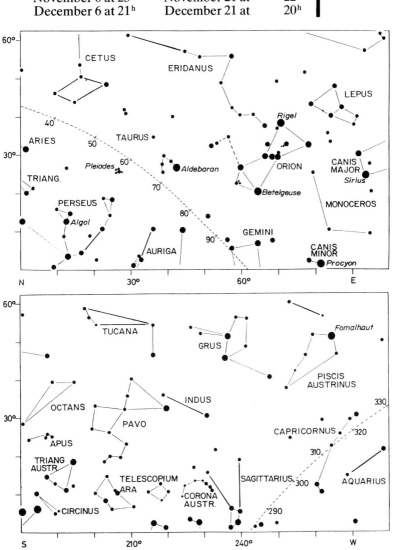

12L	September 6 at 5ʰ	September 21 at 4ʰ
	October 6 at 3ʰ	October 21 at 2ʰ
	November 6 at 1ʰ	November 21 at midnight
	December 6 at 23ʰ	December 21 at 22ʰ
	January 6 at 21ʰ	January 21 at 20ʰ

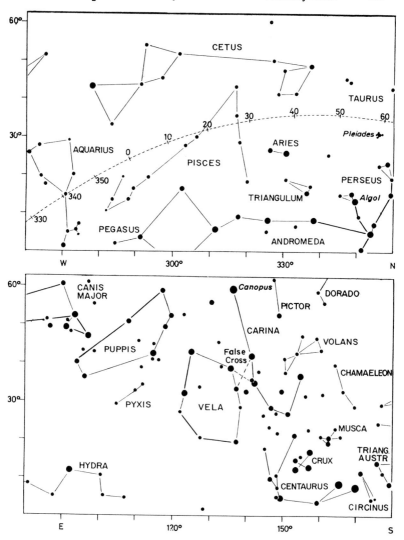

September 6 at 5^h September 21 at 4^h
October 6 at 3^h October 21 at 2^h
November 6 at 1^h November 21 at midnight
December 6 at 23^h December 21 at 22^h
January 6 at 21^h January 21 at 20^h

12R

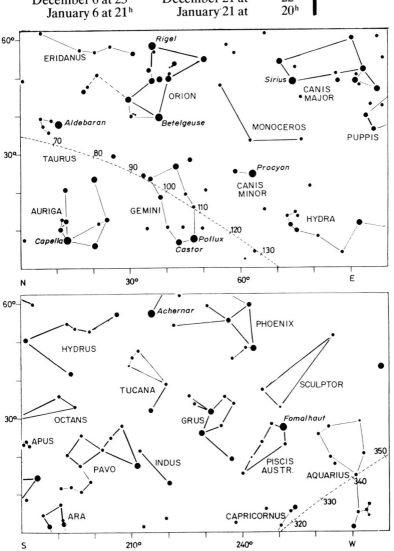

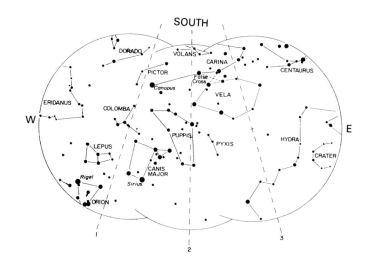

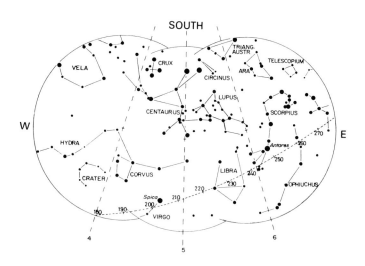

Southern Hemisphere Overhead Stars

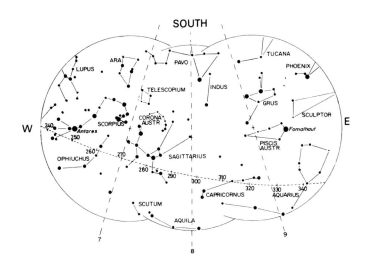

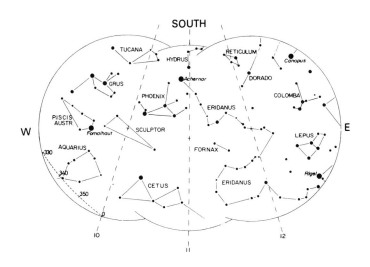

Southern Hemisphere Overhead Stars

The Planets and the Ecliptic

The paths of the planets about the Sun all lie close to the plane of the ecliptic, which is marked for us in the sky by the apparent path of the Sun among the stars, and is shown on the star charts by a broken line. The Moon and planets will always be found close to this line, never departing from it by more than about 7 degrees. Thus the planets are most favourably placed for observation when the ecliptic is well displayed, and this means that it should be as high in the sky as possible. This avoids the difficulty of finding a clear horizon, and also overcomes the problem of atmospheric absorption, which greatly reduces the light of the stars. Thus a star at an altitude of 10 degrees suffers a loss of 60 per cent of its light, which corresponds to a whole magnitude; at an altitude of only 4 degrees, the loss may amount to two magnitudes.

The position of the ecliptic in the sky is therefore of great importance, and since it is tilted at about 23½ degrees to the Equator, it is only at certain times of the day or year that it is displayed to the best advantage. It will be realized that the Sun (and therefore the ecliptic) is at its highest in the sky at noon in midsummer, and at its lowest at noon in midwinter. Allowing for the daily motion of the sky, these times lead to the fact that the ecliptic is highest at midnight in winter, at sunset in the spring, at noon in summer and at sunrise in the autumn. Hence these are the best times to see the planets. Thus, if Venus is an evening object, in the western sky after sunset, it will be seen to best advantage if this occurs in the spring, when the ecliptic is high in the sky and slopes down steeply to the horizon. This means that the planet is not only higher in the sky, but will remain for a much longer period above the horizon. For similar reasons, a morning object will be seen at its best on autumn mornings before sunrise, when the ecliptic is high in the east. The outer planets, which can come to opposition (i.e. opposite the Sun), are best seen when opposition occurs in the winter months, when the ecliptic is high in the sky at midnight.

The seasons are reversed in the Southern Hemisphere, spring beginning at the September Equinox, when the Sun crosses the Equator on its way south, summer beginning at the December

Solstice, when the Sun is highest in the southern sky, and so on. Thus, the times when the ecliptic is highest in the sky, and therefore best placed for observing the planets, may be summarized as follows:

	Midnight	*Sunrise*	*Noon*	*Sunset*
Northern lats.	December	September	June	March
Southern lats.	June	March	December	September

In addition to the daily rotation of the celestial sphere from east to west, the planets have a motion of their own among the stars. The apparent movement is generally *direct*, i.e. to the east, in the direction of increasing longitude, but for a certain period (which depends on the distance of the planet) this apparent motion is reversed. With the outer planets this *retrograde* motion occurs about the time of opposition. Owing to the different inclination of the orbits of these planets, the actual effect is to cause the apparent path to form a loop, or sometimes an S-shaped curve. The same effect is present in the motion of the inferior planets, Mercury and Venus, but it is not so obvious, since it always occurs at the time of inferior conjunction.

The inferior planets, Mercury and Venus, move in smaller orbits than that of the Earth, and so are always seen near the Sun. They are most obvious at the times of greatest angular distance from the Sun (greatest elongation), which may reach 28 degrees for Mercury, or 47 degrees for Venus. They are seen as evening objects in the western sky after sunset (at eastern elongations) or as morning objects in the eastern sky before sunrise (at western elongations). The succession of phenomena, conjunctions and elongations, always follows the same order, but the intervals between them are not equal. Thus, if either planet is moving round the far side of its orbit its motion will be to the east, in the same direction in which the Sun appears to be moving. It therefore takes much longer for the planet to overtake the Sun – that is, to come to superior conjunction – than it does when moving round to inferior conjunction, between Sun and Earth. The intervals given in the following table are average values; they remain fairly constant in the case of Venus, which travels in an almost circular orbit. In the case of Mercury, however, conditions vary widely because of the great eccentricity and inclination of the planet's orbit.

		Mercury	*Venus*
Inferior conj.	to Elongation West	22 days	72 days
Elongation West	to Superior conj.	36 days	220 days
Superior conj.	to Elongation East	36 days	220 days
Elongation East	to Inferior conj.	22 days	72 days

The greatest brilliancy of Venus always occurs about 36 days before or after inferior conjunction. This will be about a month *after* greatest eastern elongation (as an evening object), or a month *before* greatest western elongation (as a morning object). No such rule can be given for Mercury, because its distance from the Earth and the Sun can vary over a wide range.

Mercury is not likely to be seen unless a clear horizon is available. It is seldom seen as much as 10 degrees above the horizon in the twilight sky in northern latitudes, but this figure is often exceeded in the Southern Hemisphere. This favourable condition arises because the maximum elongation of 28 degrees can occur only when the planet is at aphelion (farthest from the Sun), and this point lies well south of the Equator. Northern observers must be content with smaller elongations, which may be as little as 18 degrees at perihelion. In general, it may be said that the most favourable times for seeing Mercury as an evening object will be in spring, some days before greatest eastern elongation; in autumn, it may be seen as a morning object some days after greatest western elongation.

Venus is the brightest of the planets and may be seen on occasions in broad daylight. Like Mercury, it is alternately a morning and an evening object, and it will be highest in the sky when it is a morning object in autumn, or an evening object in spring. The phenomena of Venus given in the table above can occur only in the months of January, April, June, August and November, and it will be realized that they do not all lead to favourable apparitions of the planet. In fact, Venus is to be seen at its best as an evening object in northern latitudes when eastern elongation occurs in June. The planet is then well north of the Sun in the preceding spring months, and is a brilliant object in the evening sky over a long period. In the Southern Hemisphere a November elongation is best. For similar reasons, Venus gives a prolonged display as a morning object in the months following western elongation in November (in northern latitudes) or in June (in the Southern Hemisphere).

The superior planets, which travel in orbits larger than that of the Earth, differ from Mercury and Venus in that they can be seen opposite the Sun in the sky. The superior planets are morning objects after conjunction with the Sun, rising earlier each day until they come to opposition. They will then be nearest to the Earth (and therefore at their brightest), and will then be on the meridian at midnight, due south in northern latitudes, but due north in the Southern Hemisphere. After opposition they are evening objects, setting earlier each evening until they set in the west with the Sun at the next conjunction. The change in brightness about the time of opposition is most noticeable in the case of Mars, whose distance from Earth can vary considerably and rapidly. The other superior planets are at such great distances that there is very little change in brightness from one opposition to another. The effect of altitude is, however, of some importance, for at a December opposition in northern latitudes the planets will be among the stars of Taurus or Gemini, and can then be at an altitude of more than 60 degrees in southern England. At a summer opposition, when the planet is in Sagittarius, it may only rise to about 15 degrees above the southern horizon, and so makes a less impressive appearance. In the Southern Hemisphere, the reverse conditions apply; a June opposition being the best, with the planet in Sagittarius at an altitude which can reach 80 degrees above the northern horizon for observers in South Africa.

Mars, whose orbit is appreciably eccentric, comes nearest to the Earth at an opposition at the end of August. It may then be brighter even than Jupiter, but rather low in the sky in Aquarius for northern observers, though very well placed for those in southern latitudes. These favourable oppositions occur every fifteen or seventeen years (1956, 1971, 1988, 2003) but in the Northern Hemisphere the planet is probably better seen at an opposition in the autumn or winter months, when it is higher in the sky. Oppositions of Mars occur at an average interval of 780 days, and during this time the planet makes a complete circuit of the sky.

Jupiter is always a bright planet, and comes to opposition a month later each year, having moved, roughly speaking, from one Zodiacal constellation to the next.

Saturn moves much more slowly than Jupiter, and may remain in the same constellation for several years. The brightness of Saturn depends on the aspects of its rings, as well as on the distance from Earth and Sun. The rings were inclined towards the Earth and Sun in 1980 and are currently near their maximum opening. The next passage of both Earth and Sun through the ring-plane will not occur until 1995.

Uranus, *Neptune*, and *Pluto* are hardly likely to attract the attention of observers without adequate instruments.

Phases of the Moon 1991

New Moon	First Quarter	Full Moon	Last Quarter
d h m	d h m	d h m	d h m
Jan. 15 23 50	Jan. 23 14 21	Jan. 30 06 10	Jan. 7 18 35
Feb. 14 17 32	Feb. 21 22 58	Feb. 28 18 25	Feb. 6 13 52
Mar. 16 08 10	Mar. 23 06 03	Mar. 30 07 17	Mar. 8 10 32
Apr. 14 19 38	Apr. 21 12 39	Apr. 28 20 58	Apr. 7 06 45
May 14 04 36	May 20 19 46	May 28 11 37	May 7 00 46
June 12 12 06	June 19 04 19	June 27 02 58	June 5 15 30
July 11 19 06	July 18 15 11	July 26 18 24	July 5 02 50
Aug. 10 02 28	Aug. 17 05 01	Aug. 25 09 07	Aug. 3 11 25
Sept. 8 11 01	Sept. 15 22 01	Sept. 23 22 40	Sept. 1 18 16
Oct. 7 21 39	Oct. 15 17 33	Oct. 23 11 08	Oct. 1 00 30
			Oct. 30 07 10
Nov. 6 11 11	Nov. 14 14 02	Nov. 21 22 56	Nov. 28 15 21
Dec. 6 03 56	Dec. 14 09 32	Dec. 21 10 23	Dec. 28 01 55

All times are G.M.T.
Reproduced, with permission, from data supplied by the Science and Engineering Research Council.

Longitudes of the Sun, Moon and Planets in 1991

DATE		Sun	Moon	Venus	Mars	Jupiter	Saturn
		°	°	°	°	°	°
January	6	285	174	301	58	131	296
	21	300	358	319	60	130	298
February	6	317	220	340	65	128	300
	21	332	49	358	70	126	302
March	6	345	228	14	76	125	303
	21	0	60	32	83	124	304
April	6	16	272	52	92	124	305
	21	30	114	69	99	124	306
May	6	45	304	87	108	126	307
	21	59	152	103	116	127	307
June	6	75	349	120	126	130	307
	21	89	201	134	135	132	306
July	6	103	24	147	144	135	305
	21	118	235	155	153	138	304
August	6	133	76	157	163	142	303
	21	147	279	151	172	145	302
September	6	163	130	142	183	149	301
	21	178	323	142	192	152	300
October	6	192	168	149	203	155	300
	21	207	356	161	213	158	300
November	6	223	218	177	224	160	301
	21	238	45	192	234	162	302
December	6	253	252	210	245	164	303
	21	269	83	227	255	164	305

Longitude of *Uranus* 282°
Neptune 285°

Moon: Longitude of ascending node
Jan. 1: 299°   Dec. 31: 280°

Mercury moves so quickly among the stars that it is not possible to indicate its position on the star charts at a convenient interval. The monthly notes must be consulted for the best times at which the planet may be seen.

The positions of the other planets are given in the table on the previous page. This gives the apparent longitudes on dates which correspond to those of the star charts, and the position of the planet may at once be found near the ecliptic at the given longitude.

Examples

In the Southern Hemisphere two planets are seen in the north-western sky one evening early in May. Identify them.

The southern star chart 4L shows the sky from W→N in early May and shows longitudes 110°–180°. Reference to the table on p.71 gives for May 6, the longitude of Mars as 108° and Jupiter 126°. No other planets are in this area.

The positions of the Sun and Moon can be plotted on the star maps in the same manner as for the planets. The average daily motion of the Sun is 1°, and of the Moon 13°. For the Moon an indication of its position relative to the ecliptic may be obtained from a consideration of its longitude relative to that of the ascending node. The latter changes only slowly during the year as will be seen from the values given on the preceding page. Let us call the difference in longitude of Moon-node, d. Then if d = 0°, 180° or 360° the Moon is on the ecliptic. If d = 90° the Moon is 5° north of the ecliptic and if d = 270° the Moon is 5° south of the ecliptic.

On June 21 the Moon's longitude is given as 201° and the longitude of the node is found by interpolation to be about 290°. Thus d = 271° and the Moon is about 5° south of the ecliptic. Its position may be plotted on northern star charts 3L, 4L, 5R, 6R and 7R: and southern star charts 2L, 2R, 3R, 4R, 6L, 7L and 7R.

Events in 1991

ECLIPSES

There will be three eclipses, two of the Sun and one of the Moon.

January 15–16: annular eclipse of the Sun – Australasia, Antarctica.
July 11: total eclipse of the Sun – the Americas.
December 21: partial eclipse of the Moon – Iceland, Greenland, the Americas, Australasia, Asia, N. Scandinavia.

THE PLANETS

Mercury may be seen more easily from northern latitudes in the evenings about the time of greatest eastern elongation (March 27) and in the mornings around greatest western elongation (September 7). In the Southern Hemisphere the dates are May 12 (morning) and November 19 (evening).

Venus is visible in the evenings until July and in the mornings from September to the end of the year.

Mars is visible in the evenings until September.

Jupiter is at opposition on January 29.

Saturn is at opposition on July 27.

Uranus is at opposition on July 4.

Neptune is at opposition on July 8.

Pluto is at opposition on May 10.

JANUARY

New Moon: January 15   *Full Moon:* January 30

EARTH is at perihelion (nearest to the Sun) on January 3 at a distance of 147 million kilometres.

MERCURY attains its greatest western elongation on January 14 (24°). Observers in equatorial and southern latitudes will be able to see the planet low in the south-eastern sky before dawn, throughout the month. However, for observers in northern temperate latitudes the planet is too far south of the Equator for it to be suitably placed for observation.

VENUS is slowly moving outwards from the Sun and can be seen for a short while in the evenings after sunset, low in the south-western sky. Its magnitude is −3.9. Although observers in the Southern Hemisphere are slightly better placed for observation even they will find that Venus has set within an hour of sunset.

MARS is a bright evening object in Taurus, between the Pleiades and the Hyades. Although opposition occurred at the end of last November it is still visible for the greater part of the night. Figure 2, given with the notes for February, shows the path of Mars amongst the stars. The magnitude of Mars suffers a comparatively rapid decline during January, from −1.0 to −0.1.

JUPITER reaches opposition on January 29 and thus is visible to observers throughout the hours of darkness. It is a brilliant object (magnitude −2.6) in Cancer as will be seen in Figure 1, which shows its path amongst the stars throughout the year. At opposition Jupiter is 644 million kilometres from the Earth.

SATURN passes through conjunction on January 18 and therefore remains too close to the Sun for observation throughout the month.

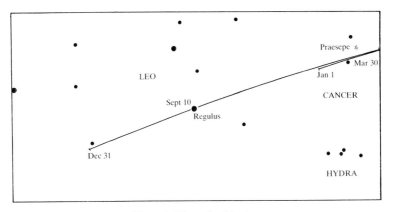

Figure 1. The path of Jupiter.

ANNULAR ECLIPSES OF THE SUN. An annular (Latin *annulus*, a ring) eclipse occurs when the Moon is in the further part of its orbit, and does not appear quite large enough to cover the Sun completely, so that a ring of sunlight is left showing round the lunar disk. Some eclipses are total along part of the track and annular along the rest, but this month's eclipse is not total from anywhere on the Earth's surface. It is seen from parts of Australia and New Zealand – not from Europe, as it occurs near midnight G.M.T.

Annularity may at times last for over twelve minutes, but it cannot be said that there is any comparison with a total eclipse, as the corona and prominences cannot be seen. The next annular eclipses will be those of 1992 (January 4) and 1994 (May 10), both visible from the Mexico and Pacific areas. There is no annular eclipse visible from Britain before the end of the century, though there will, of course, be a total eclipse on August 11, 1999 – visible from Cornwall; some people have already booked their hotel accommodation!

JUPITER AT ITS BEST. Jupiter, at opposition this month, is still well north of the celestial equator, so that British and many North American observers will be able to follow it continuously for more than a whole rotation – remembering that the rotation period of Jupiter is less than ten hours. There have been remarkable changes there in the past year or two; the South Equatorial Belt, which had for some time been the most prominent belt on the disk, virtually vanished in 1989, while the Red Spot showed a revival. There was also a curious though short-lived yellowness in the Equatorial Zone.

Of course, no Earth-based observations can hope to compete with the results from the Pioneers and Voyagers, but it is worth noting that at the present moment there is no space-craft monitoring changes there, so that planetary observers are very much on the alert. The Galileo probe, launched in 1989, will not reach Jupiter before 1995, so that we have a long wait.

CAPELLA AND VEGA. Only two brilliant stars can pass very close to the zenith or overhead point as seen from European latitudes: Capella (in winter) and Vega (in summer). Their magnitudes are almost exactly the same – Capella 0.08, Vega 0.03 – but they are very different, as Vega is bluish and Capella yellowish. Capella is the more remote of the two, at 42 light-years as against only 26 for Vega.

In case of any doubt, look for the triangle of fainter stars close beside Capella; these three – Epsilon, Zeta and Eta Aurigæ – are nicknamed the 'Kids'. Epsilon and Zeta are long-period eclipsing binaries, but they are not associated, and merely happen to lie in much the same direction as seen from Earth.

FEBRUARY

New Moon: February 14   *Full Moon:* February 28

MERCURY is not visible to observers in northern temperate latitudes but, for observers further south, continues to be visible low in the south-eastern sky before dawn, for the first half of the month.

VENUS, magnitude −3.9, continues to be visible as a brilliant evening object low in the western sky. By the end of the month, for observers in the British Isles, it may still be seen low in the sky two hours after sunset. Because of the rapid northward motion of Venus, Southern Hemisphere observers will still only be able to see the planet for about an hour after sunset.

MARS continues to be visible as a prominent object in the evening sky. During the month it will be seen to be moving slowly eastwards in Taurus, passing 8°N. of Aldebaran on February 22 (see Figure 2). Mars has a reddish tint which is an aid to identification, but Aldebaran is of the same colour. When the two objects are at their closest Mars is 0.7 of a magnitude brighter.

JUPITER, just past opposition, is a brilliant object, magnitude −2.6, and visible for the greater part of the night. At sunset it is already low in the eastern sky.

SATURN remains too close to the Sun for observers in northern temperate latitudes. Observers further south could start looking for the planet after the middle of the month, very low in the south-eastern sky shortly before the morning twilight inhibits observation. Its magnitude is +0.6.

JOHN ADAMS WHIPPLE. One of the early pioneers of astronomical photography, J. A. Whipple, died in Boston in 1891. He was born at

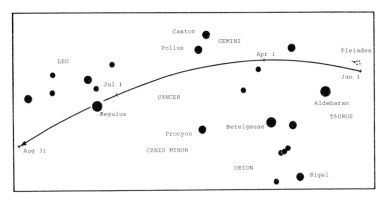

Figure 2. The path of Mars.

Grafton, Massachusetts, and became a manufacturer of chemicals for Daguerreotype processes, and with a colleague, Albert Litch, opened a gallery in Boston in 1844. He first photographed the Moon in 1849, and in the following year he and William Cranch Bond, the first Director of the Harvard College Observatory, used the 'great' 15-inch refractor to obtain an excellent series of Daguerreotypes of the Moon; lunar images five inches in diameter were put on display in London during the 1851 Exhibition. In July 1850 Bond and Whipple also managed to take the first photograph of a star – Vega, using an exposure of 100 seconds – and followed this with a photograph of Castor showing it as elongated, though the two components were not clearly separated.

In 1856 Whipple went into partnership with J. W. Black, and joined G. P. Bond, who had succeeded his father at Harvard, in new attempts at stellar photography. Bond wrote: 'On the 27th of April, impressions were first obtained from the double star Mizar (Zeta Ursæ Majoris) and Alcor (g Ursæ Majoris) in its immediate vicinity all at a single exposure by the collodion process, in eighty seconds. We have, however, since ascertained that the principal star requires but two or three seconds only to afford a decided image.'

Whipple gave up active photography in 1874, but he deserves to be remembered as one of the great pioneers in this field.

BETELGEUX: A RED SUPERGIANT. Betelgeux, or Alpha Orionis – a name which may be spelled in various ways: Betelgeuse and Betelgeuze are other variants – is the brightest of all stars which are markedly variable (unless we include Eta Carinæ, which is in a class of its own, and has not been clearly visible with the naked eye for more than a century now). The fluctuations seem to have been first announced by Sir John Herschel in 1840, though he recorded that he had noted them as early as 1836. In 1852 Herschel made it the brightest star in the northern hemisphere of the sky.

In the Cambridge catalogue the range is given as 0.40 to 1.3, and Betelgeux is classified as semi-regular with a period of 2110 days; in the *Atlas Coeli* the range is the same, but the period 2070 days. However, it is clearly impossible to give a really precise period, and one never quite knows how Betelgeux will behave. There is little doubt that it can sometimes become brighter than magnitude 0.4; it can clearly surpass Procyon (0.38) as it did, for example, in late 1967 and early 1968. It is seldom as faint as Aldebaran (0.85). However, it is an awkward star to estimate visually; its fluctuations are slow, and when using the only really helpful comparisons – Procyon, Aldebaran, Rigel (0.12) and Pollux (1.14) – allowance must be made for extinction, which is by no means easy.

During early 1990 the magnitude hovered around 0.6, markedly inferior to Procyon but superior to Aldebaran. Despite the difficulty of estimating it, visual observations of it can be useful.

It is, moreover, the star with the largest apparent diameter, and the latest techniques have shown a 'hot spot' on its surface, representing a giant convection cell; this was achieved in 1989 by P. Warner and J. Baldwin, using the 4.2-metre William Herschel Telescope at La Palma.

It had already been predicted that the outer layers of red supergiants should consist of a relatively few convection cells which, so to speak, 'bubble up' from below. Betelgeux has an apparent diameter of around 50 milliarcseconds; this is not much, but is greater than that of any other star. Warner and Baldwin perfected a new technique. They covered the 4.2-metre mirror with an opaque mask, leaving a few holes which would reflect the light from Betelgeux. The beams were then re-combined to form characteristic interference patterns, which could be converted back to produce an image of the star itself. When this was done, the 'hot spot' was clearly identifiable.

Betelgeux (dignified as Alpha Orionis, though it is seldom the rival of Rigel, which is Beta Orionis) is a colossal star, large enough to contain the entire orbit of the Earth round the Sun. Its luminosity is around 15,000 times that of the Sun. The distance is given in the

Cambridge catalogue as 390 light-years, though other catalogues give around 500 light-years. The spectral type is M.2. It is worth noting that the only other M-type stars with apparent magnitudes above 2 are Antares, which is 330 light-years away, and Gamma Crucis in the Southern Cross, which is closer at a mere 88 light-years.

MARCH

New Moon: March 16   *Full Moon:* March 30

Summer Time in Great Britain and Northern Ireland commences on March 31.

Equinox: March 21

MERCURY is too close to the Sun to be observed for the first half of the month. After that it is an evening object, low in the western sky, until early in April. For observers in northern temperate latitudes this will be the most favourable evening apparition of the year. Figure 3 shows, for observers in latitudes N.52°, the changes in azimuth (true bearing from the north through east, south and west) and altitude of Mercury on successive evenings when the Sun is 6° below the horizon. This condition is known as the end of evening civil twilight, and in this latitude and at this time of year occurs about 35 minutes after sunset. The changes in the brightness of the planet are indicated by the relative sizes of the circles marking Mercury's positions at five-day intervals. It will be noticed that Mercury is brightest before it reaches greatest eastern elongation (19°) on March 27. Its magnitude on March 15 is −1.2: twenty days later it is only +1.6.

VENUS continues to be visible as a magnificent object in the western sky in the evenings, magnitude −4.0.

MARS continues to be visible as an evening object, in the constellation of Taurus. During the month its magnitude fades from +0.6 to +1.1.

JUPITER continues to be visible as a brilliant object in the night sky, magnitude −2.4, but is now setting well before dawn.

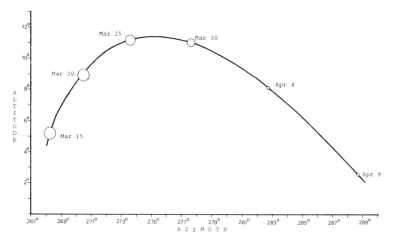

Figure 3. Evening apparition of Mercury for latitude N.52°.

SATURN is still unsuitably placed for observation by those in northern temperate latitudes. Further south, it is visible as a morning object (magnitude +0.7), low in the south-eastern sky before the sky gets too bright for observation.

PALLAS. Pallas, Asteroid No. 2, comes to opposition this month, but as it is below the seventh magnitude it is below naked-eye visibility, though binoculars will show it. Obviously, it looks exactly like a star, and the only way to identify it visually is to track its motion from night to night.

Pallas was discovered by Olbers in 1802. It has always been regarded as the second largest asteroid – much the largest is Ceres, with a diameter of 584 miles – but in fact Pallas may be slightly smaller than Vesta. The size of Pallas is well known, because it was measured in 1978 by means of the occultation technique developed by Gordon Taylor; the asteroid is triaxial, measuring 347 × 326 × 334 miles. The diameter of Vesta is not quite so well known, but two estimates give 345 miles and 358 miles respectively; the shape appears to be more spherical than that of Pallas. At any rate, Pallas and Vesta are much the same size. The only other asteroid with a diameter of over 250 miles is Hygeia (280 miles), which looks considerably fainter because it is further from the Sun.

Pallas has a carbonaceous chondritic spectrum, so that it may be similar in composition to the well-known meteorites; Ceres is much the same, though Vesta is different, and seems to have a surface covered with igneous rock. Pallas has a revolution period of 4.6 years, and a rotation period of 10 hours.

The orbit is remarkable for its high inclination, which amounts to 34 degrees (the eccentricity, 0.24, is reasonably low). It seems that either Pallas originated outside the asteroid belt, and was thrown into its present orbit by encounters with Jupiter and Saturn, or else it was perturbed into its current path by a relatively massive body which passed through the asteroid zone.

ECCENTRIC TIMEKEEPING. In Britain, March sees the start of Summer Time, when clocks are advanced by one hour to take advantage of lighter evenings. This has been the practice for many years now; during the war, and for a brief trial period subsequently, Summer Time was kept all through the year, with Double Summer Time in the summer itself. This may be reintroduced in the future, depending upon the Government mood. But in the past there have been some really eccentric methods of timekeeping – notably the Calendar of the French Revolution, which lasted from 1792 to 1806. Here there were twelve months of thirty days each, with five (or, in leap years, six) holiday days. The hour was about twice as long as the old-fashioned hour.

Even more peculiar was a scheme introduced much more recently – in fact, in 1989 – by the Leeds City Council in England. They decreed that their servants had to convert to what they called Metric Time, which divided the day into decimal fractions instead of the customary 24 hours. A Mr Kilburn, of the Leeds City Council, explained that 'An individual may wish to book time using two decimal figures, and the system will cater for this; however, it is generally accepted that one decimal place is an adequate lowest common denominator.'

It is nice to have everything made so clear. But it seems rather doubtful whether the Leeds City method will last for as long as the Calendar of the French Revolution did!

APRIL

MERCURY is visible as an evening object, very low in the western sky at the end of evening civil twilight, though only for the first week of the month, since it passes through inferior conjunction on April 14. However, for observers in equatorial and southern latitudes Mercury becomes visible as a morning object during the last ten days of the month, low above the east-north-eastern horizon at the time of beginning of morning civil twilight (see diagram in May notes).

VENUS continues to be visible as a magnificent object in the western sky in the evenings. Its magnitude is −4.1. During the middle of the month the planet passes between the Pleiades and the Hyades. The passage of the crescent Moon past the planet on April 17 will help to provide a pleasing spectacle.

MARS is an evening object, though no longer such a conspicuous object as its magnitude has fallen to +1.2. At the beginning of April Mars passes from Taurus into Gemini. Although rather better placed for observation by those in northern temperate latitudes, even they will be unable to see it easily after midnight, by the end of the month.

JUPITER continues to be visible as a brilliant object in Cancer, but not visible for long after midnight. Its magnitude is −2.2.

SATURN magnitude +0.7, is a morning object in the south-eastern sky, though not an easy object to detect for observers in the latitudes of the British Isles.

THE STAR-CLUSTERS IN THE BULL. It is sheer coincidence that Taurus, the Bull, contains what are probably the two most famous open clusters in the sky, the Hyades and the Pleiades, because there is no real connection between them; the Hyades are much the closer of the two. In Messier's catalogue the Pleiades are listed as M.45. The Hyades are not listed at all – presumably because there was no chance of confusing them with a comet; and Messier, who published his catalogue of clusters and nebulæ in 1781, was interested solely in comets.

The Pleiades, or Seven Sisters, form a relatively young cluster, and there is nebulosity between its stars; the Hyades are much older, so that nebulosity has long since disappeared. The Hyades are also much the more scattered, and are overpowered by the brilliant orange light of Aldebaran – which is rather a pity, because Aldebaran is not a member of the cluster; it merely happens to lie between the Hyades and ourselves.

Theta Tauri, in the Hyades, is a naked-eye double, made up of a white star of magnitude 3.4 and an orange companion of magnitude 3.8. With binoculars, the colour contrast is striking. The two are some 15 light-years apart, though presumably they had a common origin.

Another Messier object in Taurus is the Crab Nebula, M.1. This is certainly not a cluster; it is a supernova remnant – all that is left of the brilliant star recorded in 1054. It is well below naked-eye visibility, but with powerful binoculars it can just be seen as a dim, misty patch in the same field as the third-magnitude star Zeta Tauri.

Taurus is essentially a winter constellation to observers in the Northern Hemisphere, and by the end of spring it is lost in the evening twilight, but this year Venus lies in between the two famous clusters, and there seems to be a good opportunity here for astronomical photographers.

THATCHER'S COMET. The April Lyrid meteors rank as one of the major showers of the year, though they cannot compare with the August Perseids. The parent comet is known; it was Thatcher's Comet of 1861.

This was one of the earliest comet-meteor associations to be recognized. In 1866 the Perseids had been linked with the periodical comet Swift–Tuttle, and the Leonids to another periodical comet, Tempel–Tuttle. In Vienna, E. Weiss found that the orbit of the 1861 comet fitted the Lyrids perfectly, and this was subsequently confirmed by calculations made by Johann Galle, who traced the history of the Lyrids back to BC 687.

The Lyrid comet was discovered on April 5, 1861 by A. E. Thatcher, from New York. It was then in Draco, and was a tail-less object of magnitude 7½. It brightened as it drew inward, and at maximum brightness, in May, it reached magnitude 2½, with a tail one degree long. Perihelion was passed on June 3, and the comet was followed until September 7, when the magnitude had fallen to 10.

The comet is periodical, but as its period is around 415 years its return is not imminent! But for its undoubted link with the April Lyrids, it would not be remembered today.

MAY

New Moon: May 14   *Full Moon:* May 28

MERCURY, although it reaches greatest western elongation (26°) on May 12, is not suitably placed for observation by those in northern temperate latitudes. For observers further south this is the most favourable morning apparition of the year, the planet being visible throughout the month. Figure 4 shows, for observers in latitudes S.35°, the changes in azimuth (true bearing from north through east, south and west) and altitude of Mercury on successive mornings when the Sun is 6° below the horizon. This condition is known as the beginning of morning civil twilight, and in this latitude and at this time of year occurs about 30 minutes before sunrise. The changes in the brightness of the planet are indicated by the relative sizes of the circles marking Mercury's positions at five-day intervals. It will be noticed that Mercury is brightest after it reaches greatest western elongation.

VENUS, with a magnitude of −4.1, completely dominates the western sky in the evenings, before setting well to the north of west. Observers in the British Isles will be able to follow it until about 23^h.

MARS continues to be visible in the western sky in the evenings, magnitude +1.5. Mars is in Gemini at first, later moving into Cancer.

JUPITER is still a brilliant object in the western sky in the evenings, magnitude −2.0. By the end of the month it has set below the western horizon before midnight.

SATURN is a morning object, magnitude +0.6, visible in the south-eastern sky. Figure 5, given with the notes for July, shows the path of Saturn amongst the stars throughout the year.

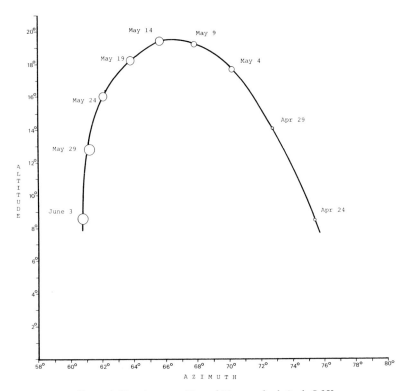

Figure 4. Morning apparition of Mercury for latitude S.35°.

THE NAMES ON MERCURY. Our knowledge of the surface features of Mercury depends upon one space-craft, Mariner 10, which made three active passes of the planet, in March and September 1974 and March 1975. Contact with it was finally lost on March 24, 1975.

Mercury proves to have a mountainous, cratered surface which looks very much like that of the Moon, though there are important differences in detail. Names had to be chosen, and this was the responsibility of the International Astronomical Union, the controlling body of world astronomy. They came up with a system which does not satisfy everyone, but does at least avoid the problem of duplication (for example, there is a crater Ptolemæus on the Moon, and another on Mars).

The Mercurian plains (*planitia*) were given the names of Mercury in various languages; for example, the Suisei Planitia is the Japanese form. The valleys (*valles*) were named after radar installations, such as Arecibo and Goldstone; ridges (*rupes*) after famous ships of exploration, such as *Endeavour* and *Resolution*; scarps (*dorsa*) after astronomers who had been particularly associated with the observation of Mercury, such as E. M. Antoniadi, whose map of the planet – drawn around sixty years ago now – was regarded as the best of the pre-Mariner era, even though it proved to be very inaccurate and Antoniadi's nomenclature was not retained. (This was not Antoniadi's fault, and it is worth remembering that his map of Mars was very accurate indeed; the Martian names we still use are largely Antoniadi's.)

There was one important exception: the largest basin on Mercury was named the Caloris Basin, because it lies at a 'hot pole', the highest temperature-region on the planet. Unfortunately only half of it was imaged by Mariner 10, and at the moment our maps of the planet are less than half complete.

The craters were named in honour of people who have made great contributions to human culture. Examples are Beethoven, Dickens, Milton, Michelangelo, Shakespeare, Wagner and Ovid. However, it has been agreed that the 20th-degree meridian of Mercury should pass through the centre of a small crater named Hun Kal, a name which stands for 20 in the language of the Maya, who used a base-20 number system. The south pole itself lies inside the crater Chao Meng-Fu.

More detailed and complete maps of Mercury must wait for a new space-craft, and as yet there are no plans for sending another mission there, so that it may be a long time before we have a really satisfactory knowledge of the surface features of this strange, hostile but intriguing little planet.

EDUARD SCHÖNFELD. This month's centenary is that of a famous German astronomer, Eduard Schönfeld. He was born in December 1828 at Hildburghausen, and was educated at Hanover and Cassel with the intention of becoming an architect. At Marburg University his early interest in astronomy was re-awakened, and he came to know F. W. A. Argelander, Director of the Bonn Observatory. From 1854 he became Argelander's assistant, and co-operated with him in the *Bonn Durchmusterung*, a very important star catalogue. In 1859 he went to Mannheim as Director of the Observatory, but in 1875 returned to Bonn as Argelander's successor. He extended the

Durchmusterung to more southern declinations, and in all charted 133,659 stars as well as making many observations of nebulæ and variable stars. Schönfeld died at Bonn on May 1, 1891.

JUNE

Solstice: June 21

MERCURY is visible as a morning object, low above the east-north-eastern horizon for a short while before dawn, though only for the first week of the month, and also only for observers in equatorial and southern latitudes, who should refer to the diagram given with the notes for May.

VENUS continues to dominate the western sky in the evenings, magnitude −4.3. During the second part of the month several planets will be seen close together as Venus passes 1°N. of Jupiter on June 17 while five days later it will be seen close to Mars.

MARS is still an evening object, magnitude +1.7, but only visible for a short while in the western sky. Observers in the British Isles will find it difficult to locate the planet because of the long duration of twilight.

JUPITER, magnitude −1.9, is still a brilliant object in the western sky in the evenings.

SATURN, in Capricornus, is a morning object, magnitude +0.4. Observers in the latitudes of the British Isles will find that by the end of the month Saturn is visible well before midnight, low in the south-eastern sky.

THE SEA-GOAT. At the moment Saturn is to be found in Capricornus, the Sea-Goat, which is one of the less distinguished of the Zodiacal constellations. No firm mythological legends seem to be attached to it, though it has sometimes been identified with the demigod Pan.

There are five stars above the fourth magnitude: Delta (2.9), Beta (3.1), Alpha² (3.6), Gamma (3.7) and Zeta (also 3.7). The constellation is not hard to identify even though it has no distinctive shape. It lies more or less between Fomalhaut and Altair, and the line of three stars of which Altair is the central member shows the way to it.

Alpha is a naked-eye double; the fainter component (Alpha¹) is of magnitude 4.2. Each is of type G, so that there is no colour contrast; each is itself double, and the fainter component of Alpha² is again double. However, the two main components are not genuinely associated. Alpha² is 117 light-years away, while the fainter Alpha¹ is highly luminous, with an absolute magnitude of −4.5, and is about 1600 light-years away. Beta Capricorni (Dabih) has a 6th-magnitude optical companion at a separation of 205 seconds of arc.

The globular cluster M.30 (NGC 7099) lies near Zeta, and is close to the limit of visibility with good binoculars. It was discovered by Messier in 1764, and has an integrated magnitude of just below 8; it is in the same binocular field as the 5½-magnitude star 41 Capricorni. The distance of M.30 has been given as 41,000 light-years; it is exceptionally poor in variable stars.

DENISON OLMSTED AND THE LEONID METEORS. Denison Olmsted, this month's centenary astronomer, was born at East Hartford, Connecticut, on June 18, 1791, and educated at Yale; he was for a time Professor at North Carolina, and afterwards Professor of Mathematics at Yale. He was one of the leading pioneers of American astronomy, and will always be best remembered because of his work in connection with the Leonid meteors.

At that time the true nature of meteors was still uncertain, and there was no known periodicity in their appearance. All this was altered by the tremendous meteor storm of the night of November 12–13, 1833. It was startling in every way, and caused a great deal of alarm, but a cosmic origin was not universally accepted; for example, a leading Washington paper stated that 'The strong southern wind of yesterday may have brought a body of electrified air which, by the coldness of the morning, was caused to discharge its contents towards the earth.'

Denison Olmsted spent the last few weeks of 1833 collecting all possible information, and found that the meteors seemed to radiate from a position in the constellation of Leo. He went on to claim that the meteors originated from 'a cloud of particles in space'. Later, the Leonids were tracked back for centuries, and were linked with the periodical comet Tempel–Tuttle.

The last major 'storm' before that of 1833 had been in 1799; there was another great display in 1866, and then another in 1966. There is a very strong chance that the Leonids will be back in force in 1999. In other years the shower is sparse, though a few Leonids are always seen on the night of November 17 in the present time.

Olmsted's work on the Leonid shower was of fundamental importance, and led to a complete change of outlook in meteoric studies. He continued to be active in research up to the time of his death on May 13, 1859.

JULY

Full Moon: July 26

EARTH is at aphelion (farthest from the Sun) on July 6 at a distance of 152 million kilometres.

MERCURY reaches greatest eastern elongation (27°) on July 25. Although the long duration of twilight renders it unobservable to those in northern temperate latitudes, observers further south will be able to see it as an evening object, low above the western horizon at the end of evening civil twilight.

VENUS is a magnificent object in the western sky in the evenings and attains its greatest brilliancy, with a magnitude of -4.5, on July 17. Venus is moving rapidly southwards in declination and for observers in northern temperate latitudes it will be disappearing in the glare of the sunset at the very end of the month. Venus and Mars are fairly close together until towards the end of the month, though there should be no danger of confusion since Mars is six magnitudes fainter, and for observers troubled by the long duration of twilight in summer, will only be detectable with some optical aid.

MARS, for observers in the British Isles, is rapidly disappearing into the long evening twilight, early in July, and will not be visible to them again this year. Further south, Mars will remain visible as an evening object in the western sky, though its magnitude is now only $+1.8$.

JUPITER continues to be visible as an evening object though only visible for a short while after dark, low above the western horizon. It is lost to view before the end of the month. Its magnitude is -1.8.

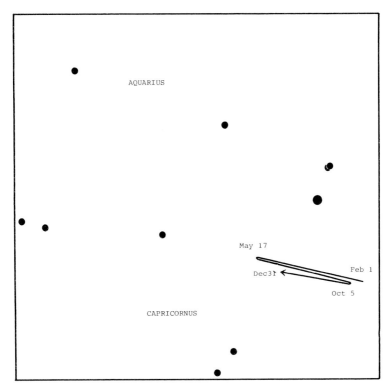

Figure 5. The path of Saturn.

SATURN reaches opposition on July 27 (magnitude +0.2), and therefore remains visible throughout the hours of darkness. Figure 5 shows the path of the planet amongst the stars. At opposition Saturn is 1338 million kilometres from the Earth.

URANUS is at opposition on July 4, in Sagittarius. The planet is only just visible to the naked eye under the best of conditions (magnitude +5.6) and in a small telescope it appears as a slightly greenish disk. At opposition Uranus is 2762 million kilometres from the Earth. Uranus is slowly catching Neptune up and in heliocentric longitude the separation is only 3½ degrees. Shortly before opposition in 1993 it will have overtaken Neptune.

NEPTUNE is at opposition on July 8, also in Sagittarius. It is not visible to the naked eye since its magnitude is +7.9. The distance of Neptune from the Earth at opposition is 4365 million kilometres.

A VERY LONG ECLIPSE. This month's total eclipse of the Sun is of special interest. Nothing of it will be seen from Britain; the track crosses Mexico, Brazil and parts of the Pacific region. It is notable because totality lasts for a very long time: 6 minutes 54 seconds. This is not far off the record. In theory, the maximum length of totality for any point on the surface of the Earth is 7 minutes 31 seconds. This has never been observed, but on June 20, 1955 totality as seen from the Philippines lasted for 7 minutes 8 seconds.

The fact that the Moon and the Sun appear so nearly the same size in our sky is a lucky coincidence – but it *is* a coincidence and nothing more. There is nothing else quite like it in the Solar System. For example, the mean diameter of the Sun as seen from Mars is 21 seconds of arc; of the two Martian satellites, Phobos has a maximum apparent diameter of 12.3 seconds of arc, and Deimos only 2 seconds of arc. However, there are some other planetary satellites which can cover the Sun completely as seen from the surfaces of their primaries and which are listed opposite.

From Pluto, Charon appears very much larger than the Sun even when Pluto is at perihelion (as it was in 1989), but of course Charon is 'locked' in the Plutonian sky, as its revolution period of 6 days 9 hours is the same as the axial rotation period of Pluto itself – a case unique in the Solar System.

Satellite transits can occur. For example, an observer on Mars will see Phobos pass across the Sun's face 1300 times in every Martian year, taking 19 seconds to cross, while Deimos would have an average of 130 transits, each taking 148 seconds. However, it is worth noting that Phobos would never rise to an observer above latitude 69 degrees north or south on Mars, while for Deimos the limiting latitude is 82 degrees.

W. M. LINDLEY. Our centenary astronomer of the month will be remembered by many readers of this *Yearbook*, as he was a very active observer, and died only nineteen years ago.

William Maximilian Lindley was born at Frankfurt-am-Main on July 27, 1891. Like his father and grandfather, he became an engineer, but he had an astronomical background (his great-

PLANET	*Apparent diameter of Sun (mean) (as seen from planet)*		SATELLITE	*Apparent diameter of satellite (as seen from planet)*	
	min	sec		min	sec
Jupiter	6	09	Amalthea	7	24
			Io	35	40
			Europa	17	30
			Ganymede	18	06
			Callisto	9	30
Saturn	3	22	Mimas	10	54
			Enceladus	10	36
			Tethys	17	36
			Dione	12	24
			Rhea	10	42
			Titan	17	10
Uranus	1	41	Miranda	17	54
			Ariel	30	54
			Umbriel	14	12
			Titania	15	00
			Oberon	9	48
Neptune	1	04	Triton	60	01

grandfather, Joseph, had been an assistant at Greenwich Observatory) and his interest dated from an early age.

At the age of fifteen he came to England, went to Sherborne School, and then graduated from Trinity College, Cambridge, in 1913. During the First World War he served on the Western Front, was awarded the M.C., and was also mentioned in dispatches. In 1919 he was demobilized, with the rank of captain, and joined the British Thomson Houston Co. in their electrical department at Rugby. Unfortunately he was unwell, and was forced to retire; in 1924 he moved to Trevone in Cornwall, where he set up a private observatory and where he remained for the rest of his life. He joined the British Astronomical Association in 1920, and became a skilled and energetic observer of variable stars; in 1939 he succeeded Felix de Roy as Director of the BAA Variable Star Section. In 1939 he joined up again, and was engaged in training recruits at

Catterick, but after a spell in hospital he was invalided out and returned to Trevone. He continued to observe variable stars and to direct the Section until his resignation in 1958. He died at Trevone on September 2, 1972.

AUGUST

New Moon: August 10   *Full Moon:* August 25

MERCURY passes rapidly through inferior conjunction on August 21. For oberservers in equatorial and southern latitudes it is an evening object for the first half of the month (magnitude +1 to +2½), low above the western horizon after sunset. For these same observers it becomes visible as a morning object at the end of August, low above the eastern horizon before dawn. By the last day of the month even observers as far north as southern Britain stand some chance of locating it given good conditions.

VENUS, for observers in the British Isles, is unsuitably placed for observation except for possibly on the last day of August when it may be detected low on the eastern horizon for a few minutes before sunrise, magnitude −4.1. For observers further south it will be an evening object until the middle of the month, low above the western horizon for a short while after sunset. It passes through inferior conjunction on August 22 and then reappears as a morning object, low in the east before sunrise, for the last few days of August.

MARS continues to be visible as an evening object low in the western sky for a short while after darkness falls, but only for observers in equatorial and southern latitudes.

JUPITER remains too close to the Sun for observation throughout the month since it is in conjunction on August 17.

SATURN, just past opposition, is visible for the greater part of the night. Saturn is in Capricornus. Its magnitude is +0.2.

THE AUGUST METEORS. As every observer knows, the Perseid meteor shower of August is the most reliable of all, and this year it should be seen at its best, as the Moon will not interfere to any great extent until the main activity is almost over. There are, however, various minor showers active during the month:

Iota Aquarids. This stream seems to consist of two rather ill-defined branches. The Southern Iota Aquarids last throughout the month, with maximum on August 6 and a ZHR (Zenithal Hourly Rate) of around 7. The Northern Iota Aquarids begin on August 11 and last into September, with maximum on August 25 and a ZHR which ranges between 5 and 10. Both streams produce meteors as bright as the third magnitude. The shower seems to have been discovered by the great amateur meteor observer, W. F. Denning, around 1800.

Alpha Capricornids. Again a shower lasting throughout August (July 15 to September 11) with a maximum on August 1. The meteors are slow, but sometimes very bright; the ZHR is around 8. Again the discoverer seems to have been Denning.

Kappa Cygnids. These persist during August (July 26 to September 1) with a rather ill-defined maximum around August 19. The shower was first reported by N. de Konkoly, the Hungarian astronomer, in 1874. The meteors are fairly fast; fireballs are sometimes seen.

Upsilon Pegasids. July 25 to August 19; maximum August 8. The ZHR is low (no more than 5) but the meteors are swift; not many show trails. The shower has not been well studied since it was first reported by H. R. Povenmire in 1975, but moonlight will not interfere this year, and meteor observers can carry out useful work.

Alpha Ursæ Majorids. August 9 to 30; maximum around August 13. This is a weak naked-eye shower, with a ZHR of no more than 4, but there are suggestions that it may produce a good many telescopic meteors.

Quite apart from these, some Delta Aquarids extend into the first part of August, and there are always sporadic meteors to be taken into account – so do not assume that every meteor seen during the month is a Perseid!

AUGUST CENTENARIES. There are two centenaries this month. Franz Friedrich Ernst Brünnow was born in Berlin in 1821, and educated at Berlin University; he became Director of the Bilk Observatory near Düsseldorf (1851) and then Breslau (1854). He went to America as Director of the Ann Arbor Observatory, but returned to Europe in 1863 as Astronomer Royal of Ireland. He was especially noted for his work on stellar parallaxes, and was an able administrator. He left Dublin in 1874 and returned to Germany; he died at Heidelberg on August 29, 1891.

Milton La Salle Humason, who was born in Dodge County, Minnesota, on August 19, 1891, had a most remarkable career. His first post at the Mount Wilson Observatory was that of a mule driver – and he never took any official scientific qualification! Yet he became one of the world's best and most respected observers, and was an invaluable assistant to Hubble in his pioneer work on galaxies. Humason became an 'official' astronomer at Mount Wilson in 1920, and undertook a tremendous amount of work in addition to assisting Hubble. Indeed, in the initial work on the distances and velocities of galaxies Hubble and Humason are inextricably linked. Humason continued his researches until his death in 1972.

SEPTEMBER

New Moon: September 8

Full Moon: September 23

Equinox: September 23

MERCURY reaches its greatest western elongation on September 7 (18°) and is visible as a morning object for the first three weeks of the month. For observers in the Northern Hemisphere this is the most suitable morning apparition of the year. Figure 6 shows, for observers in latitude N.52°, the changes in azimuth and altitude of Mercury on successive mornings when the Sun is 6° below the horizon. At this time of the year and in this latitude this condition, known as the beginning of morning civil twilight, occurs about 35 minutes before sunrise. The changes in the brightness of Mercury are indicated approximately by the size of the circles which mark its position at five-day intervals. It will be noted that Mercury is brightest after it reaches greatest western elongation. On September 1 its magnitude is +1.3 while by September 21 it is −1.2.

VENUS, magnitude −4, has now emerged from the morning twilight and may be seen low in the eastern sky before dawn.

MARS, magnitude +2.0, is now fading from visibility during the month as it disappears over the western horizon as darkness falls.

JUPITER emerges from the morning twilight at the beginning of the month and is visible low above the eastern horizon before dawn. Jupiter is to the left of Venus and 2 magnitudes fainter.

SATURN is an evening object, magnitude +0.3.

THE EARLY MORNING SKY. The eastern sky in the mornings before dawn will provide a pleasing spectacle for early risers. In the

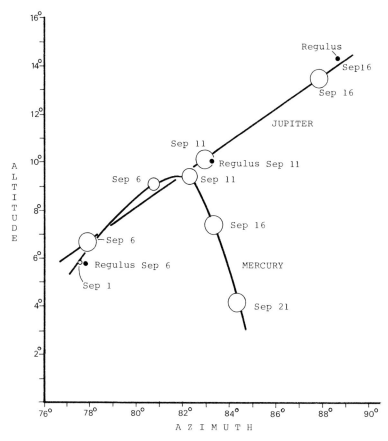

Figure 6. Morning apparition of Mercury for latitude N.52°.

following description the angular measures have been calculated for observers in the British Isles.

The brightest object will be Venus, which is then about 8 degrees south of the ecliptic and visible to the right of Mercury and Jupiter. Venus can be used as a guide to these planets, particularly between September 4 and 7 when Mercury is situated about 9 degrees to the left of Venus. If conditions are good on the morning of September 7 the old crescent Moon, only 1 day before New, may be detected in the region, being about 1½ degrees lower in altitude than Jupiter and 4½ degrees to the right. Measured from Venus the Moon is 3 degrees lower in altitude and 6½ degrees to the left. Also, Jupiter remains close to the bright star Regulus as will be seen in Figure 6.

ALBIREO. Of all the coloured double stars in the sky, perhaps the most beautiful is Beta Cygni, still known generally by its proper name of Albireo. It is the faintest member of the 'cross' of Cygnus, and is furthest away from the centre of the pattern; though it has been allotted the second letter of the Greek alphabet, it is only the fifth brightest star in the constellation. Its magnitude is 3.1, so that it is outranked by Alpha Cygni or Deneb (1.2), Gamma or Sadr (2.2), Epsilon or Gienah (2.5) and Delta (2.8).

The primary star of Albireo is of spectral type K5, and is golden yellow in colour; the distance is given in the Cambridge catalogue as 390 light-years, and the star is around 700 times more luminous than the Sun. At a separation of 34.4 seconds of arc there is a 5.1-magnitude companion of early spectral type, whose colour is usually described as vivid blue – though contrast obviously plays a part, and different observers have rather different ideas about the colour. At any rate, Albireo is a magnificent sight in any small telescope, and both components can be clearly seen with powerful binoculars.

It is very likely that the two components are physically associated, though no evidence of orbital motion has been detected since the first measurements, made in 1832 by F. G. W. Struve. The two are wide apart – at least 400 thousand million miles, and possibly much more. It is also likely that the primary is a very close binary, since it has a composite spectrum.

During evenings in late summer Cygnus is very high as seen from northern latitudes such as those of Europe; from countries such as Australia and South Africa it is low, but still accessible.

TWO MORE CENTENARIES. This year seems to be unusually rich in centenaries! Johann Franz Encke was born at Hamburg on September 23, 1791; he graduated from Göttingen University, and then went to the Seeberg Observatory, becoming Director in 1822. He achieved fame by his computation of the famous periodical comet which bears his name. The comet was seen in 1818; Encke identified it with earlier comets and predicted its return for 1822. It has a period of only 3.3 years (the shortest known) and has been seen at every subsequent return except that of 1944, when it was badly placed and when all observations were interrupted by the war. In 1825 Encke became Director of the Berlin Observatory, and in 1846 authorized his assistants Galle and D'Arrest to hunt for the new planet (Neptune) on the basis of calculations sent to him by Urbain Le Verrier. Encke retired in 1864, and died at Spandau on August 26, 1865.

Yrjo Väisälä, one of the most famous of all Finnish astronomers, was born in Kontiolahti on September 6, 1891. He graduated in 1912, and went to the Helsinki Observatory, moving next to Turku, where he became Director of the Astronomical Research Centre in 1952. His researches encompassed astronomy, optics, geodetics and meteorology. He concentrated upon planetary orbits, and developed many new optical methods; he specialized in asteroid discovery, and between 1942 and 1943 he and his team photographed more new asteroids than all the other observatories of the world managed to do between them. In addition to his numerous asteroid discoveries, Väisälä discovered three new comets. He died in Rymättymlä on July 21, 1971.

OCTOBER

New Moon: October 7   *Full Moon:* October 23

Summer Time in Great Britain and Northern Ireland ends on October 27.

MERCURY is at superior conjunction on October 3 and it is not until the last week of the month that it becomes visible low in the western sky in the evenings, to observers in equatorial and southern latitudes. Its magnitude is −1.4. It will not be visible to observers as far north as the British Isles.

VENUS is a magnificent morning object, magnitude −4.5, visible for several hours in the eastern sky before sunrise. Around the middle of the month Venus will be seen passing south of Jupiter.

MARS is not suitably placed for observation.

JUPITER is now in Leo and is a brilliant object in the eastern sky in the mornings. Its magnitude is −1.8.

SATURN, magnitude +0.5, continues to be visible as an evening object in the south and south-western skies.

THE SQUARE OF PEGASUS. During October evenings the Square of Pegasus is very prominent. Its four stars are Alpha, Beta and Gamma Pegasi, and Alpha Andromedæ – which used to be Delta Pegasi, but was transferred to Andromeda for no apparent reason.
    All four stars are between magnitudes 2 and 3, but, predictably, they are not genuinely associated, and lie at very different distances from us. Their characteristics can be summarized in a table:

Star	Proper name	Magnitude	Spectrum	Distance (lt-yrs)	Luminosity (Sun = 1)
Alpha Andromedæ	Alpheratz	2.06	A0p	72	100
Alpha Pegasi	Markab	2.49	B9	101	70
Beta Pegasi	Scheat	2.3–2.8	M2	176	300v
Gamma Pegasi	Algenib	2.83	B2	490	1320

It is interesting to compare the absolute magnitudes of the four (absolute magnitude being the apparent magnitude that the star would have if it were observed from a standard distance of 10 parsecs, or 32.6 light-years). The values are −0.1 for Alpheratz, + 0.2 for Markab, −1.4 for Scheat (variable) and −3.0 for Algenib. Thus Algenib would be much the most brilliant of the four, and would be brighter than Jupiter appears to us, while Markab would look slightly fainter than our view of Rigel in Orion. (Note, however, that the absolute magnitude of Rigel is −7, so that if seen from the standard distance it would cast strong shadows.)

Scheat is a semi-regular variable. Many lists state that it has a range of from magnitude 2 to 3, but this is too extreme; it is seldom that it rises above 2.4, and never descends below 2.8, so that it is always at least the equal of Algenib. Officially it has a rough period of 38 days, but this is subject to marked fluctuations. It is not a difficult star to estimate, because Markab makes an ideal comparison provided that due allowance is made for extinction. Even with the naked eye, the orange hue of Scheat contrasts sharply with the whiteness of the other stars in the Square, and the contrast is brought out even more strongly when binoculars are used.

A HALF-FORGOTTEN ANNIVERSARY. Many people remember that the Space Age began on October 4, 1957, with the launch of Russia's artificial satellite Sputnik 1; but how many people will recall that two years later, in October 1959, the Soviet scientists achieved another major triumph when they sent their unmanned space-craft Luna 3 round the Moon, and obtained the first photographs of the far side, which we can never see from Earth because it is always turned away from us? Luna 3 was launched on October 4, 1959, exactly two years after the flight of Sputnik 1, and sent back its pictures of the far side on October 26. By modern standards the pictures were very blurred and deficient in detail, but they did show some recognizable features, including the dark-floored enclosure known today as Tsiolkovskii.

Luna 3 was presumably intended to send back further pictures, but failed to do so, and we will never know what happened to it – but it has an honoured place in scientific history, and it proved that, as had been expected, the Moon's hidden regions are just as crater-scarred and just as barren as the regions we have always known.

NOVEMBER

New Moon: November 6   *Full Moon:* November 21

MERCURY reaches greatest eastern elongation (22°) on November 19. Although not suitably placed for observers in northern temperate latitudes, those further south will be able to see the planet as an evening object throughout the month: for them it is the most suitable evening apparition of the year. For observers in latitude S.35° Figure 7 shows the changes in azimuth and altitude of Mercury on successive evenings when the Sun is 6° below the horizon. At this time of year and in this latitude this condition, known as the end of evening civil twilight occurs about 30 minutes after sunset. The changes in the brightness of the planet are roughly indicated by the sizes of the circles which mark its position at five-day intervals. It will be noticed that Mercury is at its brightest before it reaches greatest eastern elongation. At the beginning of the month its magnitude is −0.3, while at the end it is +0.8.

VENUS, magnitude −4.3, continues to be visible as a morning object in the eastern sky before dawn. As seen through the telescope Venus goes through a cycle of phases just like the Moon. Since inferior conjunction on August 22 the percentage of the disk illuminated by the Sun has increased by the beginning of November (when it resembles the Moon at Last Quarter) until it is 50 per cent illuminated. Over the same period the angular size of the disk has decreased from 1.0 to 0.4 minutes of arc because of the increasing distance from the Earth.

MARS is at conjunction on November 8 and therefore far too close to the Sun for observation.

JUPITER, magnitude −2.0, is a brilliant object in the eastern sky in the mornings.

SATURN is still an evening object in the south-western sky, magnitude +0.6.

FAYE'S COMET. This month sees the return to perihelion of Faye's Comet, which is not likely to become bright enough to be seen with a small telescope but which has been seen at most returns since its original discovery, on November 22, 1843, by Hervé Faye at Paris. It was then 'fairly bright, with a short tail and a prominent nucleus'; the magnitude reached 5.5, so that the comet was dimly visible with

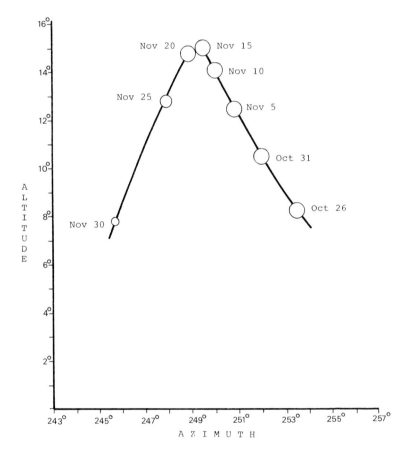

Figure 7. Evening apparition of Mercury for latitude S.35°.

the naked eye. Faye promptly calculated an orbit, and stated, quite correctly, that the period was 7½ years. It was duly recovered in 1850 by Challis, at Cambridge, but at this return the magnitude never exceeded 9½.

All subsequent returns were observed until that of 1903, after the orbit had been perturbed by a relatively close encounter with Jupiter. There were fears that it might have been lost permanently, but in 1910 Cerulli, in Italy, discovered a comet which proved to be Faye's. It was again missed in 1918, after further perturbations by Jupiter, but was recovered in 1925, and has not been missed since, though it has never become brighter than the tenth magnitude. A short tail is sometimes seen, but there are suggestions that overall the comet is now decidedly fainter than it used to be in the nineteenth century.

Hervé Faye is remembered mainly for his work upon the comet which bears his name, but he was also noted for his rather unorthodox views about the nature and constitution of the Sun. He died in 1902.

NICHOLSON'S SATELLITES OF JUPITER. Seth Barnes Nicholson, who was born a century ago – on November 12, 1891, at Springfield, Illinois – was a specialist in solar astronomy and in the determination of stellar and planetary temperatures; he began his main career at the Lick Observatory, moving to Mount Wilson in 1915.

Nicholson is one of very few astronomers to have discovered four planetary satellites – in his case all in the system of Jupiter. They are Lysithea and Carme (discovered in 1938), Sinope (his first discovery, in 1914) and Ananke (in 1951). Of these, the latter three have retrograde motion, and belong to the outer group of satellites; the fourth member of this group, Pasiphaë, had been discovered by P. J. Melotte in 1908.

All Nicholson's satellites are very small, with diameters of between twenty and thirty miles, so that they are very faint indeed, with magnitudes well below 17. They are so far from Jupiter that their orbits are by no means regular, and it is very likely that they are captured asteroids rather than bona-fide satellites. We may learn rather more about them with the arrival of the Galileo spacecraft in 1995, though it is not likely that any of the outer small satellites will be closely approached.

THE LEONIDS. The Leonid meteors, with their peak on November 17, can be spectacular – as they last were in 1966 – but are generally sparse. Not much can be expected from them this year, but there are definite hopes of another major 'meteor storm' in 1999, and it may be that activity will start to increase before then – so it may be worth keeping a watch, just in case the Leonids catch us unawares.

DECEMBER

New Moon: December 6 *Full Moon:* December 21

Solstice: December 22

MERCURY begins the month as an evening object (magnitude +1 to +2) but only for observers in equatorial and southern latitudes. After the first few days Mercury gets too close to the Sun for observation as it passes through inferior conjunction on December 8. By the middle of the month it has become a morning object (magnitude about 0) for observers in equatorial and southern latitudes, visible low above the south-eastern horizon around the time of beginning of morning civil twilight. In northern temperate latitudes the period of visibility is slightly shorter, starting around December 20 and ending when the planet reaches greatest western elongation (22°) on December 27.

VENUS is a magnificent object in the east and south-eastern skies in the early mornings for several hours before dawn. Its magnitude is −4.2.

MARS is too close to the Sun for observation.

JUPITER, magnitude −2.2, continues to be visible as a brilliant object in the morning skies. It is visible in the eastern sky before midnight and crosses the meridian before dawn.

SATURN continues to be visible as an evening object, in Capricornus, magnitude +0.7. For observers in the latitudes of the British Isles it is coming towards the end of its period of visibility and is only visible low in the south-western sky in the early part of the evening.

THE MAGNITUDES OF THE PLANETS. Venus is now at its best, and in the eastern sky before dawn it dominates the entire scene; well after sunrise it can still be seen with the naked eye if you know where to look for it. The magnitude is −4.2, far superior to any other star or planet, and two whole magnitudes brighter than Jupiter.

It is interesting to look at the magnitudes of the planets as compared with stars. The maximum magnitudes are as follows:

Mercury:	−1.9
Venus:	−4.4
Mars:	−2.8
Jupiter:	−2.6
Saturn:	−0.3

Of the outer planets, Uranus at magnitude 5.6 when at its best is just visible with the naked eye; Neptune (7.7) needs binoculars, and Pluto (13.9) requires a telescope of some size.

The only stars above magnitude zero are Sirius (−1.5), Canopus (−0.7), Alpha Centauri (−0.3) and Arcturus (−0.04). This means that the four brightest planets can outshine any of the stars apart from Sirius and Canopus, while Saturn can equal Alpha Centauri. However, Mars is very variable, and at its faintest it can sink to almost the second magnitude; Saturn's brightness depends upon the angle of its rings, and when the ring system is edgewise-on, as will next happen in 1995, the opposition magnitude will be only 0.8, equal to Aldebaran. Mercury's brilliance is never appreciated, because it is always seen against a light background, and it is not easy to realize that when at its best it is actually more brilliant than Sirius.

THE CELESTIAL RIVER. Eridanus, the River, is now on view, but it is an immensely long constellation, and only part of it can be seen from British latitudes. The brightest star, Achernar, is at declination −57 degrees, and is the nearest first-magnitude star to the south pole of the sky.

Eridanus has four stars above the third magnitude: Alpha or Achernar (0.5), Beta or Kursa (2.8), Theta or Acamar (2.9) and Gamma or Zaurak (also 2.9). Of these, Achernar and Acamar are invisible from Britain or the northern United States; on the other hand, Kursa is not far from Rigel, and could well have been included in the Orion pattern.

Acamar (declination −40°18′) is a fine double; the components are of magnitudes 3.4 and 4.5, with a separation of 8.2 seconds of arc. Both are white A-type stars, and lie at a distance of 55 light-years. There is slight relative motion, but the orbital period must be many thousands of years.

Epsilon Eridani is one of the nearest of all stars, at 10.7 light-years, and, though rather cooler and less luminous than the Sun, it and Tau Ceti are regarded as the closest stars likely to be associated with planetary systems, though at present evidence is lacking.

Eridanus covers 1083 square degrees, and is one of the largest constellations in the sky, though it must be admitted that it does not contain many objects of real interest to the user of a small telescope.

Eclipses in 1991

In 1991 there will be three eclipses, two of the Sun, and one of the Moon.

1. *An annular eclipse of the Sun on January 15–16* is visible as a partial eclipse from the south-eastern part of the Indian Ocean, the Southern Ocean, Oceania, Australasia, the western part of Antarctica and the Pacific Ocean. The eclipse begins on January 15 at 20^h 51^m and ends on January 16 at 02^h 55^m. The annular phase begins on January 15 at 22^h 00^m just off the west coast of Australia, crosses the extreme south-western part of Australia, Tasmania, the central part of New Zealand and ends on January 16 at 01^h 46^m in the South Pacific Ocean. The maximum duration of the annular phase is 7^m 55^s.

2. *A total eclipse of the Sun on July 11.* The path of totality begins in the North Pacific Ocean, passes along the western coast of Central America, crosses the centre of Colombia and ends in the centre of Brazil. The partial phase is visible from the Pacific Ocean, the southern half of North America, Central America, the Caribbean, South America except the extreme south, and the Atlantic Ocean. The eclipse begins at 16^h 29^m and ends at 21^h 43^m, the total phase begins at 17^h 23^m and ends at 20^h 49^m. The maximum duration of totality is 6^h 54^s.

3. *A partial eclipse of the Moon on December 21* is visible from Iceland, Greenland, Arctic regions, north-west of South America, Central America, North America, the Pacific Ocean except the extreme eastern part, Australasia except the extreme west, Asia except the south-western part and the extreme north of Scandinavia. The eclipse begins at 10^h 01^m and ends at 11^h 05^m. The time of maximum eclipse is 10^h 33^m when 0.09 of the Moon's diameter is obscured.

Occultations in 1991

In the course of its journey round the sky each month, the Moon passes in front of all the stars in its path and the timing of these occultations is useful in fixing the position and motion of the Moon. The Moon's orbit is tilted at more than five degrees to the ecliptic, but it is not fixed in space. It twists steadily westwards at a rate of about twenty degrees a year, a complete revolution taking 18.6 years, during which time all the stars that lie within about six and a half degrees of the ecliptic will be occulted. The occultations of any one star continue month after month until the Moon's path has twisted away from the star but only a few of these occultations will be visible at any one place in hours of darkness.

There are twenty-six occultations of planets in 1991, two of Mercury, one of Venus, two of Mars, three of Saturn, twelve of Uranus and six of Neptune.

Only four first-magnitude stars are near enough to the ecliptic to be occulted by the Moon; these are Regulus, Aldebaran, Spica, and Antares. Of these four only Antares is occulted in 1991 (4 times).

Predictions of these occultations are made on a world-wide basis for all stars down to magnitude 7.5, and sometimes even fainter. Lunar occultations of radio sources are also of interest – remember the first quasar, 3C.273, was discovered as the result of an occultation.

Recently occultations of stars by planets (including minor planets) and satellites have aroused considerable attention.

The exact timing of such events gives valuable information about positions, sizes, orbits, atmospheres and sometimes of the presence of satellites. The discovery of the rings of Uranus in 1977 was the unexpected result of the observations made of a predicted occultation of a faint star by Uranus. The duration of an occultation by a satellite or minor planet is quite small (usually of the order of a minute or less). If observations are made from a number of stations it is possible to deduce the size of the planet.

The observations need to be made either photoelectrically or visually. The high accuracy of the method can readily be appreciated when one realizes that even a stop-watch timing accurate to $0^s.1$ is, on average, equivalent to an accuracy of about 1 kilometre in the chord measured across the minor planet.

Comets in 1991

The appearance of a bright comet is a rare event which can never be predicted in advance, because this class of object travels round the Sun in an enormous orbit with a period which may well be many thousands of years. There are therefore no records of the previous appearances of these bodies, and we are unable to follow their wanderings through space.

Comets of short period, on the other hand, return at regular intervals, and attract a good deal of attention from astronomers. Unfortunately they are all faint objects, and are recovered and followed by photographic methods using large telescopes. Most of these short-period comets travel in orbits of small inclination which reach out to the orbit of Jupiter, and it is this planet which is mainly responsible for the severe perturbations which many of these comets undergo. Unlike the planets, comets may be seen in any part of the sky, but since their distances from the Earth are similar to those of the planets their apparent movements in the sky are also somewhat similar, and some of them may be followed for long periods of time.

The following periodic comets are expected to return to perihelion in 1991, and to get brighter than magnitude 15.

Comet	Year of discovery	Period (years)	Predicted date of perihelion 1990
Machholz	1986	5.2	July 22
Takamizawa	1984	7.2	Aug. 18
Hartley (2)	1986	6.3	Sept. 17
Faye	1843	7.3	Nov. 16
Shoemaker	1984	7.3	Dec. 18

Minor Planets in 1991

Although many thousands of minor planets (asteroids) are known to exist, only 3,000 of these have well-determined orbits and are listed in the catalogues. Most of these orbits lie entirely between the orbits of Mars and Jupiter. All of these bodies are quite small, and even the largest, Ceres, is believed to be only about 1,000 kilometres in diameter. Thus, they are necessarily faint objects, and although a number of them are within the reach of a small telescope few of them ever reach any considerable brightness. The first four that were discovered are named Ceres, Pallas, Juno and Vesta. Actually the largest four minor planets are Ceres, Pallas, Vesta and Hygeia. Vesta can occasionally be seen with the naked eye and this is most likely to occur when an opposition occurs near June, since Vesta would then be at perihelion. In 1991 Ceres will be at opposition on April 17 (magnitude 7.2), Pallas on March 6 (magnitude 7.1) and Juno on July 16 (magnitude 9.4).

A vigorous campaign for observing the occultations of stars by the minor planets has produced improved values for the dimensions of some of them, as well as the suggestion that some of these planets may be accompanied by satellites. Many of these observations have been made photoelectrically. However, amateur observers have found renewed interest in the minor planets since it has been shown that their visual timings of an occultation of a star by a minor planet are accurate enough to lead to reliable determinations of diameter. As a consequence many groups of observers all over the world are now organizing themselves for expeditions should the predicted track of such an occultation cross their country.

In 1984 the British Astronomical Association formed a special Asteroid and Remote Planets Section.

Meteors in 1991

Meteors ('shooting stars') may be seen on any clear moonless night, but on certain nights of the year their number increases noticeably. This occurs when the Earth chances to intersect a concentration of meteoric dust moving in an orbit around the Sun. If the dust is well spread out in space, the resulting shower of meteors may last for several days. The word 'shower' must not be misinterpreted – only on very rare occasions have the meteors been so numerous as to resemble snowflakes falling.

If the meteor tracks are marked on a star map and traced backwards, a number of them will be found to intersect in a point (or a small area of the sky) which marks the radiant of the shower. This gives the direction from which the meteors have come.

The following table gives some of the more easily observed showers with their radiants; interference by moonlight is shown by the letter M.

Limiting dates	Shower	Maximum	R.A. Dec.	
Jan. 1–4	Quadrantids	Jan. 4	$15^h28^m+50°$	M
April 20–22	Lyrids	April 22	$18^h08^m+32°$	
May 1–8	Aquarids	May 5	$22^h20^m+00°$	M
June 17–26	Ophiuchids	June 20	$17^h20^m-20°$	
July 15–Aug. 15	Delta Aquarids	July 29	$22^h36^m-17°$	M
July 15–Aug. 20	Pisces Australids	July 31	$22^h40^m-30°$	M
July 15–Aug. 25	Capricornids	Aug. 2	$20^h36^m-10°$	M
July 27–Aug. 17	Perseids	Aug. 13	$3^h04^m+58°$	
Oct. 15–25	Orionids	Oct. 22	$6^h24^m+15°$	M
Oct. 26–Nov. 16	Taurids	Nov. 4	$3^h44^m+14°$	
Nov. 15–19	Leonids	Nov. 18	$10^h08^m+22°$	M
Dec. 9–14	Geminids	Dec. 14	$7^h28^m+32°$	
Dec. 17–24	Ursids	Dec. 23	$14^h28^m+78°$	M

M = moonlight interferes

Some Events in 1992

ECLIPSES

There will be five eclipses, three of the Sun and two of the Moon.

January 4–5: annular eclipse of the Sun – west coast of North America.
June 15: partial eclipse of the Moon – Africa, America, New Zealand.
June 30: total eclipse of the Sun – South America.
December 9–10: total eclipse of the Moon – Asia, Europe, Africa, America.
December 23–24: partial eclipse of the Sun – East Asia.

THE PLANETS

Mercury may be seen more easily from northern latitudes in the evenings about the time of greatest eastern elongation (March 9) and in the mornings around greatest western elongation (December 9). In the Southern Hemisphere the dates are April 23 (morning) and October 31 (evening).

Venus is visible in the mornings until April and in the evenings from August until the end of the year.

Mars is visible in the mornings throughout the year.

Jupiter is at opposition on February 29.

Saturn is at opposition on August 7.

Uranus is at opposition on July 7.

Neptune is at opposition on July 9.

Pluto is at opposition on May 12.

The Supernova that Won't Go Away

DAVID ALLEN

On February 23, 1987 my life was changed as surely as if a volcano had erupted beneath my house. The event – the eruption itself – was, need I remind you, supernova 1987A. In common with many Southern-Hemisphere astronomers, I set aside much of the research I had been engaged in so as to study this unique and exciting event. The narcosis of the first naked-eye supernova in almost four centuries floated me into areas of science that were totally foreign to me. I was challenged to take data of a quality that befitted their likely useful life of several centuries; I was challenged also to understand what those data meant, what secrets they bore of the inner workings of one of Nature's most dramatic phenomena.

Still basking in the euphoria of a supernova in my own lifetime, I wrote my experiences into the *1989 Yearbook*. There I tried to describe the phrenetic early weeks, the succeeding hectic months, and then the gradual slowing of the pace. I ended with the comment that I was, at that stage, beginning to resume the research I had had to set aside. How wrong can I be? How naïve? Now, two years later, I come before you again, humbly, to correct that misinformation.

It had seemed a reasonable claim. Supernova 1987A was the explosion of a giant star, an event that propelled several times the mass of the Sun outwards at velocities up to nearly one-tenth that of light. The ejected gas gave out the light we recorded, and expansion adjusted its physical and chemical state. That adjustment was rapid at first, for the gas was dense and its constituent atoms jostled one another. But after a while the density fell due to the expansion, atoms scarcely met one another, and the pattern became set. Initially, measurements made on successive days could differ considerably; but as I draft these words, three years after the eruption, there is scarcely any change from one month to the next other than the inexorable halving of the supernova's brightness in response to the radioactive decay of the cobalt it produced. Why, then, does

1987A still command so much of my time? Why does adrenalin still flow every time I observe it?

Basically because it has not simply faded into oblivion as I had expected. In retrospect I can see that the first hint of its persistence came with the announcement, in March 1988, that light echoes had been found around it. To understand fully the implications of this it is useful to introduce just a tiny bit of quite simple physics.

Echoes in light

Just like sound, light can bounce off suitable objects. If you clap your hands in front of a distant cliff, you hear first the sound of the clap, and then its echo. The latter arrives later because that sound has taken a longer route. In the same way, if you were to let off a flash of light you would witness the reflection from the cliff some time after you saw the initial flash. In this case the effect of the light echo is to make the cliff briefly brighten, and the experiment is best visualized taking place at night.

Because light travels so fast, the interval between the flash and its echo would be too small to detect without sensitive equipment, being only a few millionths of a second. In the vastness of space, however, where distances are measured in thousands or millions of light-years, a delay of a year or more is perfectly possible. Not only possible, it actually is happening right now.

Imagine, if you will, a cliff near the supernova, as my cartoon (Figure 1) shows. Of course, there aren't really vast rock walls around stars, and my 'cliff' will turn out to be rather less solid. The light from the explosion of 1987A travelled directly to us, covering a distance we believe to be about 170,000 light-years. For simplicity I'll assume the number is exactly 170,000. Suppose the cliff lies two light-years away from the supernova, to the side. Then light from the flash would have travelled for two years to reach the cliff, and for a further 170,000 years from the cliff to us. It would therefore arrive two years after the flash of the supernova itself. The supernova would appear and fade, to be followed two years later by a fainter flash from the direction of the cliff. A light echo, in fact.

Figure 1 shows a cloud too. Let's say that the cloud lies 6 light-years above the supernova and 8 light-years in front. If I have correctly recalled Pythagoras' famous theorem, this puts it 10 light-years from the supernova, and 169,992 light-years from us. The light would thus travel for $10 + 169,992 = 170,002$ light-years before it reached us, again appearing two years after the supernova. We

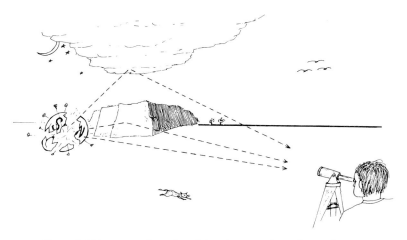

Figure 1. This cartoon shows how light echoes travel to a distant observer.

would see the cliff and the cloud light up at the same time, even though they are in very different places. I could choose many spots to place a cliff, a cloud, or the like so that the light echo arrived two years late, in early 1989. An obvious spot is one light-year directly behind the supernova: the light then travels away from us for twelve months, bounces back to pass the supernova after a further twelve months, and only then begins its 170,000 year pilgrimage.

I have had to make the second object a cloud for one simple reason. If I had put a cliff there, it would have lain almost between us and the supernova. The far side, facing the supernova, would have been lit up, but the face we see would have remained dark. However, light passes through a tenuous cloud by a process given the technical name of forward scattering. When a cloud is backlit, the light rattles off the little particles and continues towards us. The light echoes I am about to describe arise in clouds of gas and, more importantly, tiny grains of dust that scatter light very efficiently.

I have misled by portraying the supernova as a flash of light. It actually brightened steadily from late February till mid May 1987, and then began a slow decline. Each echo must do the same thing, in this case two years later. Thus a view 27 months after the outburst, in May 1989, would reveal the supernova rapidly fading whereas the echoes would all be at their brightest, and fairly constant, reflecting the light output by 1987A two years previously. Another year later supernova and echoes would each have faded, but neither would have gone out.

I listed three points from which we can receive an echo delayed by two years, and these are plotted on Figure 2, a diagram of somewhat higher scientific rigour. **A** is directly behind the supernova as seen from Earth; **B** is the cliff and **C** the cloud. These lie on a slender curve called an ellipse (for those with a technical interest, the supernova and Earth occupy the two foci). Indeed, any object capable of reflecting light and lying on that ellipse would also send back a light echo two years after the event. I have compressed on to a flat piece of paper what is actually a three-dimensional situation, and you should envisage not an ellipse but the cigar-shaped surface made by spinning this diagram about its long axis, the centre line that joins the supernova and Earth. The ellipse is not a real, visible thing. It is merely a set of places in space with the common property of introducing a two-year delay into the path to Earth.

Consider now the view from Earth. Obviously, position **A** lies

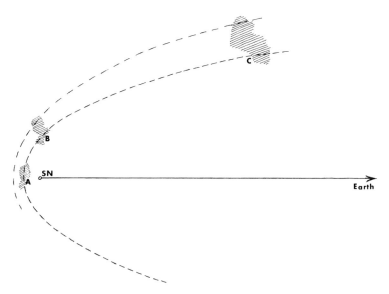

Figure 2. The inner broken line shows the location of any cloud capable of sending an echo back to Earth two years after the eruption of the supernova. As time passes, the broken line expands: the outer line shows the situation one year later again.

directly behind the supernova so is actually hidden, at least until the supernova fades. Position **B** appears off to one side, by about 2.4 seconds of arc – the angle subtended by two light-years at the distance of SN 1987A. Position **C** is 6 light-years to the side, so appears three times as far removed. Indeed, the greater the distance *in front* of the supernova that the reflecting object lies, the further to the side of the supernova will its echo appear on a photograph of the region.

This is a tremendously valuable fact. Normally when we study photographs of the sky they appear flat: we are beguiled into thinking that everything lies side by side at the same distance from Earth. In reality, of course, the stars, gas and other features are spread enormously along our line of sight. In most cases we cannot tell which are in front or behind, or by how much. In the case of the light echo we can. We have only to measure how much to the side of the supernova an echo appears, and we can determine how far in front of the supernova it arises. Only the date is needed – or rather the time since the light left the supernova. For those who like formulæ, the distance D in front is given by:

$$D = 0.34d^2/t \quad \text{light-years}$$

where d is the angle in seconds of arc between SN 1987A and the echo, and t is the time in years since mid May 1987, the epoch of greatest brilliance.

As time passes, then, the echoes change. The dotted line in the diagram shows the situation after three years have elapsed. The ellipse is now wider, so that the echo of cloud **C** appears further from the supernova. At this time there remains some faint echo light from that part of cloud **C** that was bright the year before. Observations made two and three years after the eruption therefore would show us the exact location of cloud **C** at the two points where the ellipses cross it. A series of such observations would map out the entire shape of cloud **C** *in three dimensions*, something that cannot be done in any other way. Gradually every portion fades away, but so long as there is still a dust cloud for the current ellipse to cross, a bright echo will persist. In this way the memory of the supernova can linger on long after the event itself becomes unobservable.

Rings

It was never my intention to become involved in the light echoes. I was content to study just one facet of the phenomenon, one which would cease about the end of 1990 when 1987A became too faint for the Anglo-Australian Telescope. Thus when our photographic expert, David Malin, produced the first picture of the echoes to be taken with the AAT, I looked it over with only casual interest.

As I knew from the previous announcements, the photograph, reproduced here as Figure 3, showed two rings of light around the supernova. But David is a clever chap. Whereas others had managed to photograph only partial rings, David had revealed complete circles of light. He had done this by subtracting away the stars and nebulosity that conceal and confuse the region. He hadn't actually obliterated the stars from the sky, you understand. He merely used an older photograph taken before SN 1987A appeared, and by superimposing a positive of that one and a negative of the recent plate, he had made the unwanted bits cancel out fairly well. You can see the stars as white blobs surrounded by dark rings, while the nebulosity which is quite bright hereabouts has virtually vanished altogether. That pre-supernova photograph has been one of our most valuable assets.

I knew, too, when I first saw the photograph, what the two rings meant. Had the dust grains filled an extensive region in front of the supernova, they would have produced a large haze of light. The rings told us that most of the gas and dust had been tidily swept into piles, thin sheets that lay between us and 1987A. If you could set off from the supernova towards Earth, you would travel through clear space for about 300 light-years before coming to a smoggy region not more than a few tens of light-years thick, and responsible for the inner ring. Continuing, you would traverse clear space again until you were almost 1000 light-years out, when you'd encounter another patch of smog: the outer echo.

As I glanced at the photograph I was immediately struck by something odd. Take a moment to look yourself: do you notice anything? Here's a clue: the banks of dust should make circular echoes that have the supernova at their centre. Look again and you will see that the outer echo is off-centre. The gap between it and the inner ring is greater to the upper left than to the lower right.

I went home and began some complicated algebra. It took me several hours that night before I had worked it all out. I ended up with the equation given in the previous section, though this is actually a gross simplification of the true situation, a simplification made possible only because of the extreme distance of both 1987A and the dust it illuminates. My algebra showed that the two clouds

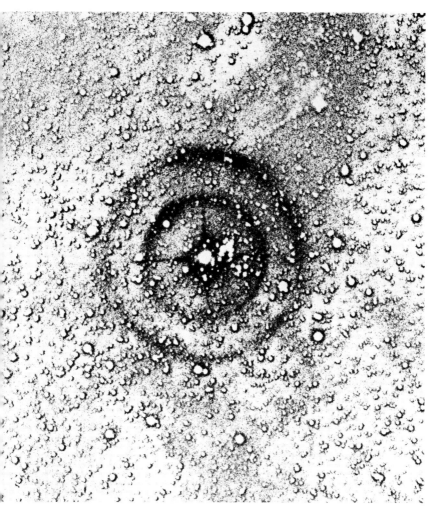

Figure 3. This is the difference between two photographs, such that features on the more recent one appear in the negative. In theory, the stars should have cancelled completely, but due to different atmospheric turbulence they were larger on the newer photograph, so have yielded dark rings with white centres. SN 1987A is the black object in the middle, with stars superimposed in white. The central of these is the star that became the supernova. Like all bright stars, 1987A has the four 'diffraction spike' arms, this time seen in black. The two dark rings are the light echoes. The photograph was taken on July 15, 1988. See also Figures 4 and 5.

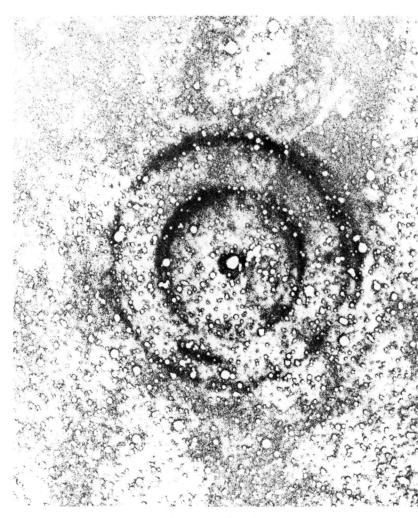

Figure 4. A photograph of the rings, made in the same way as Figure 3, dated February 6, 1989.

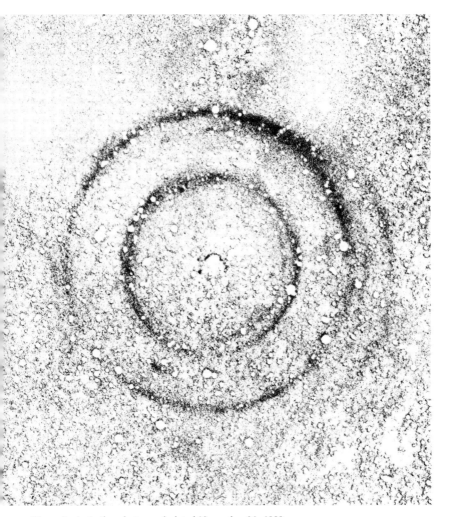

Figure 5. A similar photograph dated November 21, 1989.

lay a very long way in front of the supernova – about 400 and 1200 light-years.

The algebra had been worked out before, and I could have just dug through the literature instead. But deriving it for oneself gives a much better understanding of what is going on. In this case I quickly realized that the outer echo is off-centre because the sheet of dust is tilted. The upper left portion is further in front of the supernova than the lower right by about 150 light-years. From even a single photograph we were learning about the three-dimensional distribution of otherwise invisible material in our neighbouring galaxy the Large Magellanic Cloud.

Warrick Couch was also excited by the photograph. He, David and I began a proper analysis, as well as an observing programme to follow the changes with time and so to map out the dust completely. In a scientific paper based solely on that first photograph we concluded that we are probably seeing the front and back faces of a gigantic bubble blown by a collection of hot stars that lie to the upper left and in front of SN 1987A. The stars together form the cluster known as NGC 2044, discovered by Sir John Herschel during his survey of the southern sky from South Africa. Hot stars can blow such bubbles either by a steady shedding of excess gas or by the eruption of one of them as a supernova. In either case the outflowing material pushes the surrounding matter ahead of it like a snowplough, building up an ever denser ripple as it goes.

We now have several photographs, of which the best three are reproduced on the same scale in Figures 3, 4 and 5, and show how the rings have expanded. Some years must pass before we can show for certain that they are indeed two cuts through a single bubble. In the interim the photographs reveal plenty more of interest. Note how both rings have become split into two around one side. This seems to suggest that one bubble has been expanding into another one from a slightly different centre. The last photograph also shows a fainter, partial ring outside the other two to the right. The sheet responsible for this echo appears to be even more tilted, and we don't know its origin.

There are blobs appearing between the two rings as well, so the bubble isn't totally hollow. One of these, to lower left, became for a while just about the brightest echo feature, though it is only small. The brighter the echo, the more dust grains in the cloud where it originates. So this cloud is particularly dense. We have no idea why such a cloud resisted the snowplough action.

If you scrutinize Figures 4 and 5 you will also see a rather blobby echo immediately around the image of the supernova. There was no way to see this on the first photo because the supernova itself was still too bright, producing the burnt-out black circle in the negative. The fading of 1987A has at last enabled us to see material in close proximity. It remains a difficult study, a situation that should improve as the supernova continues to fade. There is intense interest in the immediate environs of 1987A, primarily because it can tell us something about the history of the star before its catastrophe.

According to the best theoretical accounts, the star that became supernova 1987A had a complicated life story. It started massive and hot. As its hydrogen fuel became exhausted, and different nuclear processes took over, the star had to adjust itself, growing huge and cool. In that supergiant phase it slowly shed its outer layers – something approaching ten times the entire mass of the Sun – and consequently grew smaller and hotter once more. This second hot phase was accompanied by a bubble-blowing outflow like that of the stars of NGC 2044, so that the gas shed as a supergiant was ploughed into a small, hollow bubble around the star. Before the bubble attained great size . . . *bang!* Supernova. The material shed in the supergiant phase at least partially accounts for the echo features closest to the supernova.

The ultraviolet flash

Theorists also tell us of an ultraviolet flash. If you were standing near a star that turned into a supernova, the first hint you would have of the inner catastrophe would be when a violent ripple progressing outward through the star reached its surface. Should you ever find yourself in this predicament, ensure you have strong sunglasses and a liberal coating of suntan cream, for the manifestation is a burst of ultraviolet radiation lasting maybe as much as one hour, and many million times more intense than sunlight.

Of course, the UV flash has never been seen, because supernovæ give us no advance warning, so nobody has ever been watching at the critical time. Anyway, it's all too far into the ultraviolet for our eyes. There is therefore considerable interest in verifying the UV flash by indirect methods.

Being first out, the UV flash leads the expanding light echo. We might instead be able to record extra ultraviolet radiation at the outer edge of the echo rings, but for one fact. Ultraviolet is very readily absorbed, so that it almost certainly failed to penetrate the wall of gas close in to the supernova. The interest is therefore intense in studying that innermost echo.

The ploughed-up supergiant gas suffered a violent case of sunburn as it basked in the UV flash. Ultraviolet ionizes gas to create glowing nebulæ like the famous one in Orion. Once ionized, the gas fades only slowly, taking perhaps a decade to unwind. This is a different type of light echo, but an echo all the same. In my initial analogy you can liken it to a cliff daubed with fluorescent paint. We are now watching the slow fading of the paint.

As the gas fades, the radiation it emits tells of the physical and chemical state and is amenable to study by spectroscopy. The ionized gas around SN 1987A was discovered even before the outer echoes became visible, and has become much easier to study as the supernova faded.

Infrared spectra

Spectroscopy of the ejected material has, from the outset, been the optical astronomer's most valuable tool to understand the entire phenomenon. I teamed up with Peter Meikle and Jason Spyromilio, from Imperial College in London, to pursue infrared spectroscopy. Peter is the driving force behind the study, a quiet, competent physicist who contrasts so dramatically with Jason, young and flamboyant, that the three of us make quite a comedy act when together at the telescope. This appearance belies a deal of hard work, particularly by Peter, Jason, and students at Imperial College, to interpret the excellent data we have garnered.

Infrared spectroscopy of supernovæ was a new field, and we were lucky to find that some of the most important clues to the entire supernova phenomenon lay there, awaiting our study. Like eighteenth-century explorers, we charted unmapped terrain and made exciting discoveries. As the nineteenth century progressed the oceans and land masses of the world became known so that exploration lost much of its romance; in the same way the supernova settled down to become predictable as it began to fade from our view. In this endeavour, therefore, the phrenetic pace eased.

Or so I thought, two years ago. But I had failed to consider the ultraviolet flash and its attendant echo. So, just as the subject had become routine, we began to see a spectral feature whose intensity remained constant as 1987A faded. With each observation this feature seemed to rise from the ashes of the star, and to dominate the spectrum more.

The feature was caused entirely by helium. And it, too, proved to be another vital clue to the supernova. I have not the space to enter into the rather complex physics of the situation. Suffice to say that three months of our research went into understanding what was going on, and we emerged with clear evidence of two important pieces of information.

First, the supergiant phase didn't generate a spherical bubble of gas. Instead, the star chose to throw off material in a narrow spray on one side, or perhaps in two opposite directions. There is mounting evidence that this so-called bipolar pattern is not at all uncommon in many celestial situations, but astronomers argue about how it comes to pass. By finding an example in this star we have eliminated some of the possibilities. The orientation of the outflow parallels the elongation in the supernova's ejected material that has been recorded by several techniques. Somehow SN 1987A knew its precursor had a favourite direction in space, and preferred that direction despite the star's total devastation.

Second, we were able to measure the mix of hydrogen and helium in the gas, finding much more of the latter than is normal in the universe. But this is exactly what was predicted by the theoreticians. In its supergiant phase 1987A threw off gas that had resulted from the conversion of hydrogen to helium. The proportion of the two had been predicted; our observations verified that prediction.

Will it ever go away?

At this stage in the evolution of supernova 1987A I could reasonably expect to have virtually finished with it. Instead of that, I am engrossed in two continuing studies of different versions of the echo. Both require considerable work over several years more. Ah well – it is this very unpredictability that gives research its appeal.

Can I even guess when 1987A really will 'go away' and let me continue the research I was doing in 1986? I have learnt not to be so rash. After all, there is a huge mass of gas billowing outwards at high speed, heading for an inevitable collision with the material shed by the supergiant. It should arrive some time in the 1990s. When it does, dramatic things will ensue: events never before witnessed. We will drop everything we are doing to study the happening in great detail; and adrenalin will flow faster yet.

The Biggest Structures in the Universe

A. P. FAIRALL

What are the biggest physical structures in the Universe? Up to around fifteen years ago, we thought them to be clusters of galaxies, at most 10 million light-years in size. Today the picture is totally different; structures up to 1000 million light-years across are recognized – but that is only the minimum, our mappings have still not reached the scale where the Universe can be said to be homogeneous. More remarkably, the new findings have revealed a gigantic foam-like texture to the Cosmos. This seems surprising since foam-like formations more usually occur on a very small scale, such as in bath sponges or even soapsuds. Whatever the resemblance or connection, it seems as though a great new key to understanding the fabric of the Cosmos is being presented to us.

Why did we not know about these structures much sooner? Because we are not able to view the three-dimensional distribution of galaxies at all readily. When we photograph the sky (Figure 1), we get a two-dimensional view. For instance, if we look at the wide-angle survey photographs from the Palomar, UK and European Schmidt telescopes, we see plenty of galaxies – if you look closely enough, you can see thousands of them on each photograph (except for photographs aimed into the thick of the Milky Way). Of course, while each photograph may show thousands of galaxies, it also shows millions of stars. However, the stars are all very much in the foreground, contained in our home Galaxy. Each galaxy we see may in itself contain towards a million million stars, but in general the galaxies are too distant for the stars to be seen individually. It's like viewing a distant city by night; you see the collective light and not the individual street lamps.

Galaxies have one big advantage over stars. Stars appear as pinprick images on the photographs, whereas galaxies show disks, although these get very small as the galaxies get more distant. Although there is a mixture of big and small galaxies, in general you can get a feel for the distances of galaxies by comparing their

Figure 1. Astronomers at Oxford University have completed the largest survey of galaxies in an area covering 10 per cent of the sky reveals long, thin, curving lines of galaxies in an 'voids'. Each photograph (originals are 14 inches square) shows about 150,000 stars and 50,000 galaxies. This picture shows a typical patch of sky represented by a single dot in the final distribution map of 2,000,000 galaxies; the image on the left is the original photograph, that on the right shows the same area of sky as stored in the survey after processing by the Automatic Plate Measurement machine (reproduced by courtesy of the Department of Astrophysics, University of Oxford).

THE SPATIAL DISTRIBUTION OF GALAXIES

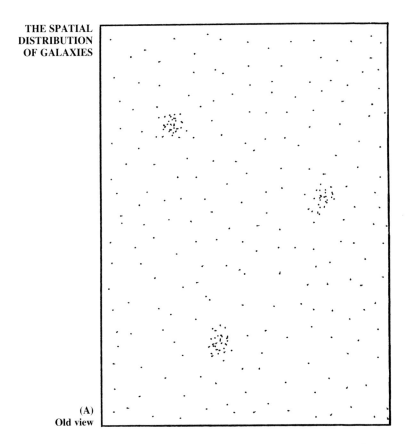

(A)
Old view

Figure 2. The dots in these diagrams represent galaxies. (A) For many years, the clusters of galaxies were thought to be superimposed on a random 'field' component of galaxies. The clusters were believed to be the largest structures in existence. However, the modern picture (B) reveals a 'foam-like' distribution with the galaxies not scattered randomly but surrounding empty voids.

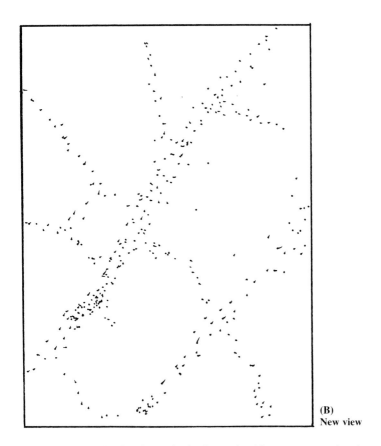

(B)
New view

apparent sizes in the sky. It is similar to looking out over a landscape and using the apparent sizes of trees and lesser foliage to gauge distances in the landscape. When there are no trees, such as in the Apollo photos from the surface of the Moon, one has no perspective of distance (the mound behind the astronauts in the Apollo 15 photographs is really a mountain 20,000 feet high). Anyway, this was the technique used independently, in the 1950s and 1960s, by two great pioneers of extragalactic astronomy, George Abell and Fritz Zwicky, to gauge the relative distances of the clusters of galaxies on the Palomar Sky Survey. The picture that emerged was one of occasional clusters superposed on a general random 'field component' of clusters (see Figure 2). However, Zwicky and others (particularly C. P. Shane and Gerard de Vaucouleurs) suspected that much larger entities existed – the superclusters. What nobody realized was that there were actually regions devoid of galaxies. That could only come when much more accurate distances of galaxies could be determined.

Whilst it takes a fair deal of effort just to get the distance of a single galaxy, it is generally easier to get the distance of a galaxy than the distance of a star, thanks to the well-known Hubble law. Our Galaxy is not expanding, so, in general, the distances to the other stars in our Galaxy are not increasing. But the Universe is expanding and the distances to the other galaxies are increasing, so they appear to be moving away from our Galaxy. It goes according to the Hubble relationship

$$V = Hd$$

where V is the speed of recession from our Galaxy, d is the distance and H is a constant, the so-called Hubble constant. In other words, if a neighbouring galaxy is moving away from us at 100 kilometres per second, the next but one neighbour would be moving away at 200 kilometres per second, the one after that at 300 kilometres per second and so on. Don't worry about every one trying to move away from our Galaxy. There is nothing wrong, because you get the same pictures from every other galaxy. In fact, it is not really so much that the galaxies themselves are in any way making themselves move in this way, but rather that the intervening spaces have been given a sort of Alice-in-Wonderland pill that makes them grow. The important thing is that if you measure the velocity of recession of a galaxy, then you can determine its distance. This assumes you know the value of the Hubble constant, and there is currently some controversy as to what its exact value should be, but a middle-of-the-road value is 20 kilometres per second of velocity for every million light-years of distance.

So far, so good; now we just have to set up to measure the velocity of recession of the galaxy. We do this by obtaining a spectrum of the galaxy – an observation that takes a large telescope from a few minutes to much longer according to the brightness of the galaxy. Superimposed on the colours of the spectrum are key spectral features, but, when a galaxy is receding away from us, the Döppler Shift moves these towards the red end of the spectrum. Measuring this shift gives us the velocity of recession, and from the velocity of recession we get the distance. With modern technology, this sort of observation is now very much faster than it used to be. In the early 1960s, a typical spectrogram took some hours to obtain using the largest telescopes in the world. Nowadays, with image intensifiers and photon-counting detectors, the same observation can be carried out with a much more modest telescope in only a few minutes. As a result, while there were only about a thousand redshifts available in 1960, today there are more like around 40,000.

One more complication – while the velocity of recession of a galaxy is mainly due to the cosmological expansion, there can also be a contribution from the galaxy's own peculiar motion – perhaps up to several hundred kilometres per second. This could be one of two things. First, if the galaxy is a member of a reasonably dense cluster or if it is one of a pair, then it must have a form of orbital motion (otherwise gravity would make the cluster collapse). Second, even if the galaxy is fairly isolated from its neighbours, then it may still participate in large-scale streaming motions. Our Galaxy is such a case; it apparently is streaming at some 600 kilometres per second.

It's very difficult to sort out all these peculiar motions, and since they are generally much smaller than the cosmological expansion, we initially overlook them and simply take velocity as representing distance. Figure 3 (Southern redshift plot) is a good example. It can be seen that the distribution is anything but uniform. Where there is an adequate density of points, an astonishing foam-like structure emerges. There are regions almost void of galaxies that form the 'bubbles' in the foam. It is the scale of the structure that is remarkable – the bubbles shown are up to 100 million light-years across (or, if you prefer, 1000 million million million kilometres).

Foam-like structures normally occur on very much smaller scales, and usually in aqueous or organic media. It is also quite amazing to find such similar structure displayed, not by a continuous medium, but by a large number of unconnected point-like systems (on this scale, even the galaxies have shrunk to points); it would seem quite surprising if the air molecules inside a room suddenly adopted a foam-like distribution – and quite against the respected laws of thermodynamics! But then, whilst the galaxies might be moving, their motions are very slow when measured against the very large-scale foam-like structure. Either this is the distribution the galaxies had when they were formed, or, since their formation, they have been slowly drawn into these foam-like formations. Whatever the

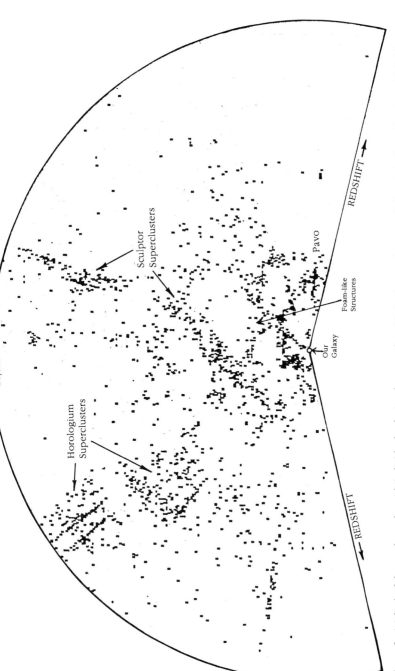

Figure 3. A 'slice' of the southern sky with individual galaxies shown as dots. Their distance from our Galaxy is indicated by the redshift (the perimeter of the diagram corresponds to a velocity of recession of 20,000 kilometres per second). This reveals a cross-section of the foam-like structure and supercluster network. The voids are typically empty, save for a few galaxies lying inward from the surrounding walls.

case, here is a great clue as to how the Cosmos evolved just before or after the formation of galaxies.

Theories abound as to how this sort of structure came about. If gravity is responsible, then there is much too little mass in the galaxies for it to have a significant effect. Thus, the most established of current cosmological hypotheses is 'Cold Dark Matter'. This theory considers that the galaxies are only a tiny portion of all the matter present. Much more mass means much more gravity – enough to draw the galaxies towards concentrations and create superclusters. It is not clear, however, that a network of superclusters will necessarily adopt a foam-like texture. If the matter were not pulled by gravity, could it have been pushed instead – by gigantic explosions, for instance? This is one of the competitive theories, which envisages a sort of 'cosmological baking powder' to give the structure of the Universe the texture of a cake! Perhaps the most novel current theory concerns cosmic strings – the spaghetti-like leftovers from the very early Universe. Almost immeasurably thin, yet incredibly massive, they could sweep through space with galaxies formed in their wake. At this stage there is no easy telling which theory is right and which is wrong.

But the story of large-scale structure in the Universe is not yet finished, for every time we extend our surveys deeper, we find ever larger structures. The foam-like bubbles are by no means the largest entities. Rather, superclusters connect and align to make even larger structures – and the foam-like texture fills in the intervening spaces. The diagrams that accompany this article show great long structures – massive filaments, or even perhaps two-dimensional walls of galaxies.

Where does this place our own position? Figure 4 is a schematic indication of where our Galaxy is situated relative to neighbouring structures. The band of obscuration that lies horizontally across the diagram is due to the plane of our own Milky Way galaxy. Our Galaxy lies towards the fringe of the Virgo supercluster, so named after the Virgo cluster that lies at its centre. However, as the diagram suggests, the Virgo supercluster looks a little anæmic compared with other neighbouring structures, nor is it completely isolated from them. Filamentary links appear to stretch out towards the Hydra–Centaurus–Pavo conglomeration. In fact, our Galaxy, and presumably most of our neighbours, is streaming in the Centaurus direction at 600 kilometres per second. Not that we will ever get there – the Centaurus concentration is moving away at 4500

Figure 4. A schematic diagram (the dots are not real data), based on various redshift maps, to indicate neighbouring structures out to a redshift of several thousand kilometres per second. The plane of the paper conveys a general tendency for these structures to favour a 'supergalactic' plane.

kilometres a second due to the expansion of the Universe. However, this streaming motion has given rise to the idea of there being considerable mass in Centaurus, the so-called 'Great Attractor' whose gravitational pull has set our Galaxy in motion. In any case, part of the motion may be due to an imbalance in local structure, since neighbouring voids lie in the opposite direction. Also in the opposite direction is the dominant Perseus–Pisces supercluster – and it is not clear why we are not pulled that way. Perseus–Pisces has a filamentary core but links to structures in Sculptor (see Figure 3). In another direction still, and also separated from Virgo by voids, is the Coma supercluster, centred around the dense Coma Cluster. Shown in Figure 4 in cross section, it is really a thick two dimensional sheet, often termed a 'great wall'. Its full extent is still not known for there is still much mapping to be done. For the moment, the surrounding structures almost give a 'tree-ring' appearance, with us in the centre – but that is certain to change as the maps are extended.

It is an exciting era to live in. For the first time in mankind's history, we are seeing structures that are significant on the scale of the whole observable Universe (with horizon at around 15,000 million light-years). A new fabric of the Cosmos has been revealed. We must now decide how it was woven.

Jeremiah Horrocks and the Transit of Venus, 1639

ALLAN CHAPMAN

Renaissance Europe witnessed the making of many discoveries in the natural world, from Columbus' first landfall in the Americas in 1492, to Harvey's realization that the blood circulated around the body in 1628. But of all the emerging sciences, astronomy underwent the fastest development, building as it did upon foundations laid down in the ancient world, and modified by Copernicus and Tycho Brahe. So much of this development, however, hinged upon evidence gained by instruments which measured, rather than just looked at nature, and when Galileo first applied the telescope to astronomy in 1610, a whole cluster of new discoveries followed.

Most of these discoveries related to the Solar System, and came to establish plausible arguments in favour of Copernicus' theory that the Earth went around the Sun. Yet the astronomical Renaissance was a product of Continental discovery, with such figures as Tycho Brahe the Dane, Kepler the Austrian, Galileo the Italian and Gassendi the Frenchman, and one looks in vain for eminent English contributions in the early days. Not until Jeremiah Horrocks successfully predicted and observed the first recorded Transit of Venus on November 24, 1639, can it really be said that English astronomical discovery began.

Horrocks' observation of the Transit of Venus would not have been possible but for a series of developments which had taken place over the thirty preceding years. The most important of these had been the invention of the telescope in 1609–10, followed by Kepler's three Laws of Planetary Motion. The early telescopic views of the planets, moreover, had indicated that they were spherical worlds in their own right, and not just lights in the sky, and when Pierre Gassendi watched the black dot of Mercury pass across the Sun's disk in 1631, it was clear that they were opaque as well. Jeremiah Horrocks, who clearly took the mathematical initiative in the events which led up to the 1639 Transit of Venus observation, was familiar with all of these discoveries, as his surviving writings show, and urged his astronomical friend William Crabtree to also keep his eyes open and provide confirmation.

Transits of Venus across the Sun are very rare, and are occasioned by the respective orbital velocities and inclinations of Venus and the Earth. Venus completes a full circuit of the Sun in 224.7 days as opposed to the Earth's 365.25, so that Venus needs 19 months to catch up with and overtake the Earth from each conjunction. The orbits of the two planets are also inclined to each other at an angle of 3°23′39″, so that the plane of Venus' orbit cuts that of the Earth at the two nodal points. The Earth passes these nodal points in space twice in the course of a year, around June 6 and December 6 (or May 24 and November 24 in the 'Old Style' calendar), so that for half of the 19 months Venus is inclined above the Earth's orbital plane, and for the next 9½ months is below it (see Figure 1).

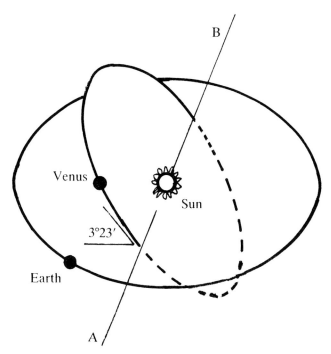

Figure 1. The inclination of the orbits of Venus and the Earth at 3°23′. Only when Earth, Venus and the Sun occupy positions on the line A–B at the same time can a Transit occur.

For most of the time, the nodal points are unoccupied as the Earth passes by them, for Venus has already 'ascended' or 'descended' into the upper or lower parts of its orbit. Very rarely, however, a complex series of orbital cycles which takes just over 100 years to complete will occur, and Venus will arrive at its nodal point at the same time as the Earth. The Earth, Venus and Sun will momentarily occupy points on the same straight line, and Venus will appear sharply defined in transit on the face of the Sun.

Over the last 350 years only five such transit alignments have taken place, in 1639, 1761, 1769, 1874, and 1882. As one can see from the sequence, transits fall in pairs eight years apart, but with a duration of between 105½ and 121½ years between pairs. There have been no transits in the twentieth century, and the next pair will occur in 2004 and 2012.

The first astronomer to recognize that Venus *could* possibly transit the Sun had been Kepler, who correctly predicted that a Transit would take place in the late autumn of 1631. Though it was searched for by Gassendi, no one observed it because the Transit took place when the Sun was below the horizon for European observers, and only visible in western America, where no astronomers were active in 1631. Kepler predicted that no further Transit would occur until 1761.

It was in this respect that Jeremiah Horrocks displayed a remarkable originality. Familiar as he was with Kepler's work, he came to realize in October 1639 that the impending nodal crossing of Venus due in late November would fall so close to the Sun that a Transit would take place. He grasped the crucial point that while Kepler was correct in his prediction of the century or so separation between Transits, they occurred not *singly*, but in *pairs* eight years apart.

Compared with the European giants whose work he so admired, Horrocks was a young man who held no position. The recently deceased Kepler, on the other hand, had been an Imperial Professor, Tycho Brahe a Danish aristocrat enjoying Royal patronage, and Galileo a senior Italian academic and friend of the Grand Duke of Tuscany. Horrocks, by contrast, was the twenty-year-old son of an obscure Lancashire farmer in 1639, with no real job or prospects. In every sense of the word, he was an *amateur* astronomer, and perhaps the first outstanding English example of that noble breed.

He had been born near Bolton, Lancashire, in 1619, though his childhood was spent in the region of Toxteth, Liverpool, before entering Emmanuel College, Cambridge, as a 'Sizar' or poor scholar, in 1632. Sizars worked as servants in their colleges in return for a free education, and Horrocks left in 1635, after four years, without taking his degree. If this strikes us as odd today, one must bear in mind that the ritual of taking a degree was expensive in the seventeenth century, and many poor men never 'supplicated' for them after completing their studies. After all, a letter of recommendation from one's tutor, a fluency in Latin and a firm grasp of dogmatic theology sufficed for most prospective employers.

Horrocks would have received little or no formal mathematical training in Cambridge, for in those days one did not choose to 'read' for a degree in a specific subject as one does today. There was only one curriculum for all students, and it consisted of classical languages and literature with a good deal of Protestant Theology. Emmanuel was one of the most intellectually rigorous colleges in Cambridge in the early seventeenth century, the radical theological tendencies of which have inclined many later writers to include Horrocks as one of its numerous 'puritan' graduates. Though we know from his writings that Horrocks was a deeply religious man, we have no evidence that he was a 'puritan' in the political or theological sense.

Though some mathematically related lectures were delivered, they were generally regarded as tangential to the main course, and whatever astronomy Horrocks had picked up at Emmanuel, he would have acquired by private study. While no one would have gone out of his way to provide formal instruction in the astronomy of Copernicus, Galileo or Kepler, no one, by the same token, would have prohibited it. There was nothing remotely heretical about these ideas in England; it was simply that they were not part of the course of study. On the other hand, a student was quite at liberty to study them privately, as a spare time pursuit.

As a man trained in Latin and Greek, Horrocks would have found the international world of scientific literature easily accessible to him in the libraries and bookshops of Cambridge. In the absence of firmer information one presumes that it was through this avenue of private study that Horrocks gained his intimate familiarity with the latest astronomical and mathematical ideas of his day, and while relatively poor, owned at least one book. This was a copy of Philip Lansberg's *Tabulæ*, which still bears his signature, and was presented to Trinity College, Cambridge, in 1841 by Augustus de Morgan.

Following his return to Lancashire in 1635 at the age of seventeen, he made the acquaintance of William Crabtree of Salford, near Manchester. How the two men came to know each other is uncertain, but it was probably through a mutual acquaintance from Manchester named John Worthington. Worthington and Horrocks were contemporaries at Emmanuel, and while we know nothing of his mathematical relationship with Horrocks and Crabtree, we know that Worthington must have known several other Cambridge contemporaries who later became eminent in astronomy and science. These included John Wallis, who came up in 1633, Seth Ward and Ralph Cudworth. Worthington lived on to become a Cambridge dignitary, and Wallis one of the first Professors of Astronomy at Oxford. It was also Wallis, as a Fellow of the newly founded Royal Society in the 1660s, who first brought the work of the deceased Horrocks before the wider scientific world. If one thinks, however, that Horrocks and some of his contemporaries were precocious when entering University at thirteen or fourteen, one must remember that an undergraduate education was much more elementary in the seventeenth century than it is today, and one generally took one's B.A. at seventeen or eighteen and the M.A. at twenty-one.

William Crabtree, however, was not a University man, but a clothier or cloth dealer, of Salford. Nine years older than Horrocks, he had received a good formal education in Manchester in the 1620s, and was a comfortably-off businessman married into one of the leading families of the district when he first came to exchange letters with Horrocks in 1636.

What both Horrocks and Crabtree had in common was an interest in practical astronomical observation, and a desire to substantiate for themselves the 'New Astronomy' of Copernicus, Galileo and Kepler. Between 1636 and 1639 their surviving letters indicate an extraordinary activity and originality. Horrocks was the real intellectual leader and innovator in the relationship, but Crabtree provided invaluable cross-checking of observations, discussion and encouragement. During this three-year period, Horrocks demonstrated the elliptical shape of the Lunar orbit in accordance with Kepler's Laws, and used an occultation of the Pleiades by the dark edge of the Moon in 1637 to show that the stars were mere points of light. Horrocks argued that if they possessed finite diameters – traditionally said to be two minutes – their light should have faded gradually as they were occulted, rather than being snuffed out instantly. The two astronomers also studied the orbital shapes and possible law-like behaviour of comets.

Horrocks was an assiduous planetary observer, although unlike most modern astronomers, what interested him were not the surface details of the planets, but their orbital positions with relation to the Sun and stars. As a man who was convinced that not only did all of the planets rotate around the Sun, but that they did so in accordance with the precise geometry of Kepler's Laws, Horrocks measured planetary positions in an attempt to substantiate these Laws. Most astronomers in the early seventeenth century, one must remember, did not actually *observe* the heavens direct when it came to advancing cosmological arguments, but used the positions of the planets computed from the Ephemeris tables. Even by the time that he was seventeen, however, Horrocks had come to realize that all of the current tables were shot through with errors, though the best available – the *Rudolphine Tables* of Kepler – had at least been calculated from the direct observations of Tycho rather than having been derived from earlier tables.

Horrocks was familiar with most of the standard tables currently in print, and judging from his critical appraisal of their faults, probably possessed several copies of his own. The letters which he exchanged with Crabtree bristle with his annoyance against these unreliable books, and convinced him, and his friend, that no progress was possible in astronomy so long as one depended on them. But neither Horrocks nor Crabtree possessed the princely resources necessary to build an observatory like that of Tycho Brahe. Instead, they devised wooden instruments of their own which exploited the natural geometrical ratios of triangles.

We know quite a lot about the instruments with which Horrocks had been measuring planetary positions over the years from 1636 to 1639 from their description in his surviving letters to Crabtree. His favourite angle-measuring device was the 'astronomical radius', which consisted of a T-shaped pair of jointed wooden rods about one yard long (Figure 2). In use, the end of the long arm of the T would be held up to the eye, similar to the way in which one sighted a crossbow, while a metal sighting pin was slid along each short cross arm of the T. These sighting pins would be adjusted so that when any pair of celestial objects were precisely enclosed between them when viewed from the end of the long arm, a triangle was formed. As Horrocks knew the length of the long arm to start with, and could easily measure the linear distance enclosed between the

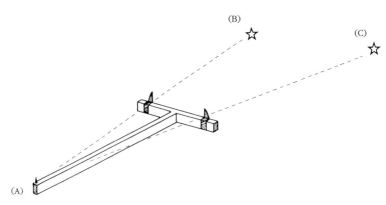

Figure 2. Horrocks' 'Astronomical Radius' or 'Cross Staff'. The observer's eye would have been at A and he would have sighted the stars B and C against the upright pins, to produce a triangle. As the length of the long rod remains unaltered, being the imaginary radius of a circle, the proportions formed by the positions of B and C for any observation provide the variable chord lengths from which the angle A can be computed.

sights, it was simple to compute the exact angle subtended as a tangent or chord function. He made several versions of this straight-forward yet very effective instrument to measure a variety of large and small angles, which he could build up into an extensive catalogue of original observations.

It was from a combination of practised personal observations of the planetary motions, and a growing distrust in the values given in the standard tables (especially those of Philip Lansberg the Belgian) which led Horrocks to realize that a Transit of Venus across the Sun's disk would probably take place on the autumn node of 1639. All the tables disagreed as to the exact point where Venus' orbit would cut the apparent Solar orbit on the day of its crossing, November 24, Old Style (or December 6, New Style) 1639. Where they all did agree, however, was that the nodal point would be near to the Sun.

Though Horrocks does not tell us in detail how he came to arrive at his prediction of the Transit, it was probably the result of inspired guesswork based on an average node derived from all the tables, checked and confirmed with his own independent values for Venus' orbit based on previous observations. But no matter how he derived the figure, he realized that if the Transit did take place, it would be more than just an academic feather in his cap, but a crucial cross-check on the shape of Venus' orbit. As astronomers possessed much more accurate values for the place of the Sun in the sky than they did for Venus, he realized that once the planet became visible on the Solar disk, one could obtain a vastly more accurate value for the nodal point by relating it to the Sun's centre.

Much of the drama of the event also stemmed from the fact that Horrocks had only predicted the impending Transit about a month before it was due, and hurriedly wrote to Crabtree on October 26, 1639 beseeching him to keep watch. We know that the word was also passed on to Samuel Foster via Crabtree (who may still have been in touch with Worthington in Cambridge), and to Jeremiah's brother, Jonas Horrocks, in Liverpool.

By the autumn of 1639, Horrocks was residing in the parish of Much Hoole a few miles outside Preston, Lancashire. Although we do not know his business there, popular legend made him out to be the curate of the parish. This cannot have been the case, however, for at the age of twenty, Horrocks was well under the minimum age for Ordination. More likely, he probably had the job of tutor to the children of one of the local gentry families, or may have been an assistant master in a school. Both occupations were common ones for young University men without degrees or connections. The assumed clerical status of Horrocks derived entirely from his subsequent statement that upon the Sunday when the Transit took place he was occupied with duties of a 'higher calling', though as a tutor or teacher responsible for the catechizing of his charges, he would have been just as fully occupied on the Lord's Day as any curate.

It was by the thorough way in which he conducted the Transit observation that showed him to be a skilled and practised astronomer. In the little treatise which he later wrote describing the event, Horrocks resolved to observe the Transit by projecting the Solar image through a small refracting telescope on to a screen (Figure 3). The screen was inscribed with a 6-inch diameter circle, the horizontal diameter of which was divided into thirtieth divisions to correspond approximately to the minutes of the Solar diameter, while the circumference was divided into 360 carefully drawn degrees (Figure 4). This arrangement enabled him to record the position of Venus on the Sun's disk, determine the precise time of ingress by calculation, relate the planet's centre to that of the Sun, and derive the exact point of the node (Figure 5).

November 24, 1639 was a dull day, and on those occasions when Horrocks' duties permitted him to check the sky, he found no Sun.

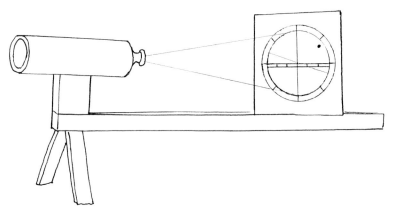

Figure 3. Reconstruction of Jeremiah Horrocks' apparatus used to observe the Transit of Venus. The telescope is being used to project an image of the Solar disk on to the screen. The black dot of Venus is seen entering into the divided circle of the screen. Though Horrocks does not explicitly state that the telescope and screen were attached to a connecting bar, as shown in the illustration, it would have been impossible otherwise to have maintained an accurate alignment.

Not until 3.15 in the afternoon, when the Sun was within a few degrees of the western horizon, did it shine through, and Horrocks was quick to align its image on his screen. He was delighted to find the black circular dot of the planet already silhouetted upon the edge of the Solar disk, and over the next half hour of visibility, secured three separate fixes as it moved. Because he had divided the circumference of his screen into degrees, he was able to establish that the ingress began 62½° from the vertical on the projected image. When he compared the diameter of the image of Venus to the overall diameter of the Sun, he computed that the planet subtended an angle of 1′12″ or at most 1′30″.

The first thing which impressed Horrocks was the smallness and intense blackness of the image of Venus. Gassendi, indeed, had been struck by the smallness of the image of Mercury in transit in 1631, though Horrocks expected Venus to be bigger as it is much brighter than Mercury. Seventeenth-century astronomers knew nothing about the reflectivity of the Venusian clouds, and the contribution which they made towards the planet's brilliance.

During the half hour observation time, Horrocks was able to calculate that the planet had moved 1′24″ across the Sun, from which he was then able to calculate the direction of the Transit path,

VENUS ON THE SUN'S DISC

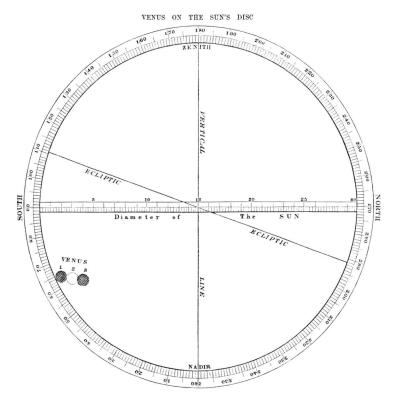

Figure 4. Horrocks' projection screen showing the three observed positions of Venus, seen between 3.15 and 3.45 p.m. on Sunday, November 24, 1639. In his Venus in Transit (1859 translation, see bibliography) pages 124–5, he states that Venus appeared on the screen at the top right hand quadrant, 62½° from the vertical. In this published engraving, however, he showed the position in the bottom left hand quadrant, as it was 'out of doors beneath the open sky', and not telescopically inverted on the screen in the 'dark apartment'. In the reconstruction in Figure 3, the position of Venus is shown in its inverted, or observed position.

its closest approach and probable time to the Sun's centre, and from these, the nodal point. Brief as his observation was:

> 'I was enabled by Divine Providence, to complete so effectually that I could scarcely have wished for a more extended period.'

Horrocks then rhetorically asked how many other astronomers had seen this remarkable phenomenon? and concluded that there

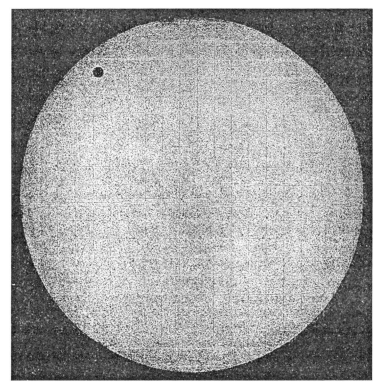

Figure 5. Photograph of the Transit of Venus taken in June 1874. The appearance of Venus in the 1874 Transit would have been in a different quadrant of the Solar disk than in 1639. The 1639 Transit took place when Venus approached the descending *node, whereas in 1874, Venus approached her* ascending *node.*

were no others, apart from his friend William Crabtree, who had used a technique identical to his own, and drawn similar conclusions. There is no evidence that Horrocks' brother Jonas saw anything. But none of the giants of Continental astronomy had seen it, preferring to rely on their tables rather than look at the heavens direct, while the 'profoundly ignorant' astrologers had failed to a man to foresee the event.

In the composition of his *Venus in sub sole visa*, or *Venus in transit across the Sun*, wherein Horrocks described in detail his observations, he also displayed a mastery of those skills of argument which would have lain at the heart of his education at Emmanuel.

Realizing that critics might draw all sorts of alternative conclusions from what he and Crabtree had seen, he set out to forestall their arguments and demolish the opposition before it got off the ground. Quite apart from his polemic against those conservative astronomers who had simply missed the Transit, he next addressed himself to the question of whether the object seen actually was Venus. He discussed sunspots and general blemishes on the Solar disk, but pointed out that the object seen in Transit was, in spite of its unexpected smallness, too big, black and round to have been mistaken for a sunspot. The object which he had observed, moreover, possessed an independent motion, travelling across one-twentieth of the Sun's disk in half an hour.

Horrocks then proceeded to use his three observations, made respectively at 3.15, 3.35 and 3.45 p.m., to correct the elements of Venus' orbit and revise the currently erroneous value for the planet's parallax. This in turn was used to extract a value for the Solar parallax, which was shown to be ten times smaller than the one currently accepted, indicating thereby that the Sun was much more remote than hitherto believed. After a detailed analysis of the discrepancies which existed between the values contained in the major tables, he re-affirmed his belief that only by looking at nature direct could any new knowledge be gained.

But we must not forget that Horrocks' *Venus in Transit* was far more than just an impartial record of an important scientific event; it was an impassioned defence of the 'New Astronomy'. Horrocks recognized the enormous interpretative mileage and polemic value of the Transit observation and how it could be used to provide substantiation for the Copernican theory and Kepler's Laws. In this respect, he followed Galileo who, thirty years before, had used his own recent discoveries with the telescope to undermine the Ptolemaic system. By the fact that Venus revealed a round, black disk in Transit, Horrocks correctly argued that the planet was a *world* and not just a light in the sky, as classical astronomy had taught. If Galileo's telescope had shown Jupiter and Saturn to be spherical worlds, and transits had revealed Mercury and Venus to be the same, then it seemed much more logical to posit that the Solar System was a system of *worlds* rotating around the *Sun*, rather than celestial quintessences rotating around the Earth.

If, as Horrocks had shown elsewhere, the Moon moved in an elliptical orbit like Mars, could not Venus' revised elements show that she moved likewise, and that Kepler's Laws ran true for the whole Solar System? He accepted Kepler's idea that in the absence of the now discredited crystalline spheres of heaven, the planets were made to rotate by a species of solar force. Horrocks had been deeply impressed by Kepler's demonstration of the exact proportional relationships existing between the physical size, orbital diameter, and velocity of the planets. The bigger planets, after all, were the furthest out from the Sun and moved the slowest. Perhaps because the invisible solar force grew weaker with distance, it was necessary to have bigger planets as one went outwards so that it had larger areas to act upon, though as the force grew progressively weaker, it moved the planets more slowly, thereby accounting for the slower velocities of the outer planets. One can see here the origins of those proportions of mass and velocity which Newton was to consolidate into his system of Universal Gravitation in 1687, and why he felt obliged in *Principia*, Book III to pay acknowledgements to Jeremiah Horrocks as well as Kepler.

Horrocks was very much concerned with the sizes of the planets, and tried to devise ways of measuring the angles which they subtended in the sky in an attempt to revise the wildly over-large figures which he felt were accepted by more conservative astronomers. He believed that the Universe was much vaster than ancient astronomy had indicated, and that improved measurements would show up the over-estimates for the physical constants and proportions in general use. Needless to say, he was delighted to find that Venus in Transit revealed an angular diameter of $1'12''$ and not the $3'$ cited in the standard tables.

He devised an ingenious naked-eye method of measuring planetary diameters using commonplace objects. Arguing that the traditionally large angular diameters ascribed to the planets derived from the light scatter which they occasioned in the eye, he started to look at them through tiny pinholes pierced through pieces of cardboard. In this way, he could cut out the glare, and make them appear much smaller. By knowing the exact diameter of the pinhole as a fraction of an inch, and moving the card away until the planet seemed to fill up the hole, he could arrive at a figure for the planet's *angular* diameter based on the tangent relationship of the pinhole to its measured distance from the eye. Using this method on the now receding Venus, for instance, in January 1640, he determined that the planet's angular diameter lay between 27 and 38 seconds of arc.

From his measures of the other planets (and inevitable over-estimates of the angular diameters of Mars and Saturn), he believed that if an observer could stand on the Sun, then *all* the planets would subtend the *same* angular diameter of 28″ when seen in conjunction. This provided further substantiation for the innate geometry and order with which he believed God had built the Universe.

The Transit of Venus of 1639 not only represented the first observation of a significant astronomical event, but provided an avenue via which a young man of extraordinary precocity could revise several Solar System constants and proceed to write a powerful little treatise in favour of the New Cosmology. It would be hard indeed to find a single half hour better spent in the whole history of astronomy, when considering the new facts and interpretations which followed from it.

Though only twenty years old when he made his observation of the Transit, Horrocks had little more than a year of life ahead of him. We know that within the next few months he left Hoole and returned to Toxteth, where he wrote up his *Venus* treatise, and started to collect materials for another, intended to deal with the dimensions of the Sun. This uncompleted work, of which nothing has survived, was probably based upon his studies of the Solar diameter conducted over the last three or four years. While Horrocks was willing to accept 31′30″ as a working average Solar diameter for his Transit of Venus calculations, he realized that if the Earth rotated around the Sun in an elliptical orbit, the apparent diameter would change slightly with the season.

It was also during this post-Transit final year of his life that his friend William Crabtree began to correspond with the Yorkshire mathematician, William Gascoigne. Gascoigne had recently invented the eyepiece, or filar micrometer, which Horrocks recognized as a valuable instrument for measuring planetary and Solar diameters, though we do not know if Horrocks ever obtained a micrometer of his own. It was Gascoigne, however, who along with Crabtree and Horrocks, made up the 'Three north country astronomers', who came to lay the foundations of an observational, instrument-based 'New Astronomy' in England. There is no evidence that Horrocks and Crabtree were acquainted with Gascoigne in November 1639, however, for he is never mentioned with relation to the Transit observations.

Whatever killed Jeremiah Horrocks did so suddenly and there is no evidence to favour the image of the poor, sickly consumptive who martyred himself for science, into which role Victorian writers liked to cast him. All that we know is that he died 'very suddenly' on the morning of January 3, 1641, the day before he had intended to ride from Liverpool to Salford to visit Crabtree. Crabtree himself recorded the fact on the back of a bundle of letters which he had received from Horrocks over the years of their friendship.

Though both Crabtree and Gascoigne died in 1644, the pioneering work of Horrocks had been recognized by several men who would bring him and his friends into posthumous prominence. His old college contemporary, John Wallis, edited the surviving mathematical letters into the *Opera Posthuma* in 1672, and the newly founded Royal Society recognized his importance by giving their imprimatur to the published work. While Horrocks' *Venus* treatise remained unpublished in England, the Danzig astronomer Johannes Hevelius published it in a Latin translation in 1662 to accompany his own observations of the 1661 transit of Mercury. Over the seventeenth and eighteenth centuries, several astronomers and antiquarians tracked down and published surviving Horrocks fragments, and even Flamsteed, the first Astronomer Royal, paid him homage.

By 1700, Horrocks had come to be recognized as the founding father of a new approach to astronomy, based not upon speculation, but upon careful observation and measurement of the heavens and the use of mathematics as the technique whereby the data should be interpreted. Deeply influenced as Horrocks had been by the examples of Galileo and Kepler, we must bear in mind that he possessed an originality which enabled him to venture into territories even beyond their reach, to forge that great linchpin in the development of gravity theory between Kepler and Newton. Whatever Horrocks might have achieved had he not died at the age of twenty-two we will never know, but what we must not forget is the significance of the 1639 Transit of Venus as the event by which the New Astronomy came of age in England.

Bibliography
Jeremiah Horrocks [Horrox], *The transit of Venus across the Sun 1639*, translated from the Latin with a 'Memorial' by A. B. Whatton (1859).
Robert Grant, *History of physical astronomy*, (1852).
John E. Bailey, 'Jeremiah Horrox and William Crabtree, observers of the Transit of Venus, 24 Nov. 1639', in the *Palatine Note-book*, II, (1882).
Allan Chapman, *Three North Country astronomers*, (1982).

Most of the primary sources of the Horrocks and Crabtree correspondence are still not available in English translation, and consist of their letters published in Jeremiah Horrox, *Opera Posthuma*, Edited by John Wallis, (1672).

The ROSAT Mission

BARRY WELSH

Exciting times in 1990 were enjoyed by European and American X-ray astronomers with the launch of the ROSAT satellite. ROSAT (an acronym for the German word 'Roentgensatellit') is a tripartite project between Germany, Britain and the USA involving the launch of two major scientific instruments which will carry out high angular resolution surveys of the whole sky at X-ray wavelengths between 6 and 600 Å. X-rays lie at the high energy end of the electromagnetic spectrum and were first discovered nearly a century ago in 1895 by the German physicist Wilhelm Roentgen. Since they possess high energy (usually measured in kilo-electron volts, or keV) they are of very short wavelength and are highly penetrating through matter. This fact is well known to anyone who has ever been to a hospital to have an 'X-ray', in which we see a shadow of our bony skeleton on a photographic plate produced by the differential passage of X-ray light through our body's flesh and bones.

X-rays are generally divided into two classes: hard and soft X-rays. As these names suggest, the hard (or highest energy) rays penetrate the furthest through matter, whilst the softer X-rays (of lower energy, and thus longer wavelength) are more easily absorbed by materials. Both these forms of high energy radiation are produced in the Cosmos by violent events in which gaseous matter is heated to temperatures well in excess of one million degrees, or by the collision of rapidly expanding shells of gas ejected by exploding stars. Under such extreme physical conditions X-ray spectral lines can be produced when electrons jump between atomic orbits with very large energy differences.

Today, our knowledge of the sky at X-ray wavelengths has come from a series of scientific satellites launched between 1970 and 1987, which include such names as UHURU, the three High Energy Astrophysical Observatories (HEAO) of which HEAO-2 known as the Einstein Observatory was the most successful instrument, the European Space Agency's EXOSAT mission, and the Japanese

Astro-D satellite, more commonly known as GINGA. To date over 1000 celestial X-ray sources have been discovered and thus we see the X-ray sky to be filled with emission from a wide variety of astronomical objects which include the coronæ (or outer atmospheres) of nearby stars, distant clusters of galaxies and the very exotic and remote compact galaxies such as quasars and BL Lacertæ objects. All these individual sources are observed against what appears to be a cosmological diffuse background of weak X-ray radiation which some astrophysicists claim holds the secret of where most of the hidden mass in the Universe actually resides.

Unfortunately for astronomers, X-rays pass through or are absorbed by most materials, and thus, unlike visible light, cannot easily be focused. Since X-rays do not reflect from most materials when they strike at large incident angles (as light does in conventional reflecting optical telescopes), new ways had to be found to focus these high energy rays. The solution to this difficult problem was to arrange for the X-rays to graze the reflecting surfaces of highly polished and smooth cylindrically shaped metal mirrors at very small incident angles. At these shallow angles the X-rays behave like stones skipping across the surface of water, and are not appreciably absorbed by the metallic mirrors. Under these conditions, known as Wolter-Schwarzschild optics, X-rays can be brought to a sufficiently good focus that X-ray images can be made of distant celestial sources. Such instruments are called 'grazing incidence' telescopes and form the basis of the design of the ROSAT instrumentation.

The ROSAT hard X-ray telescope consists of four concentric grazing incidence mirror pairs with an outer mirror aperture of some 83 cm. The telescope was designed and built in Germany under the direction of scientists at the Max Planck Institute near Munich. Its main task in orbit will be to carry out a whole-sky survey at energies between 0.1 and 2 keV at an angular resolution of about 30 seconds of arc. The two X-ray detectors that convert the incoming radiation into electronic signals are called position sensitive proportional counters (PSPC), each PSPC being able to view about two degrees on the sky at any given time. This survey will be the first with an imaging X-ray telescope and will lead to an improvement in sensitivity by almost three orders of magnitude compared with previous surveys. The survey will take six months to complete and will be followed by a period of pointed observations, lasting for at least an additional year, during which selected sources will be

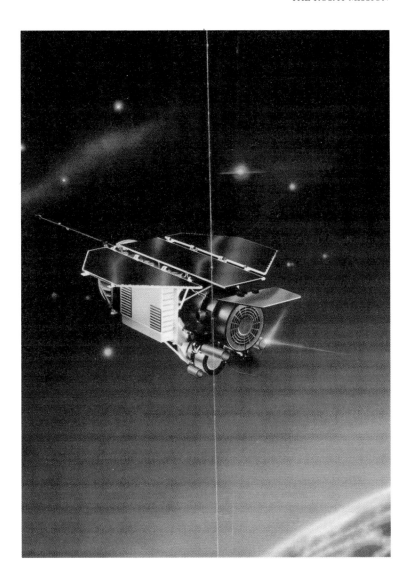

Figure 1. Artist's impression of ROSAT in orbit (copyright Dornier Gmbh).

investigated in greater detail to reveal their spatial structure, spectral energy distribution and possible time variability in their X-ray emission.

One unique aspect of the hard X-ray telescope is the addition of a high resolution imager (HRI) device in which selected sources will be investigated at a previously unimaginably high angular resolution of less than 5 seconds of arc. The HRI, which has been built at Harvard in the USA, consists of a microchannel plate X-ray detector that is capable of time-tagging incoming X-ray photons which appear in its half-degree field of view to within 60 microseconds. Although the HRI has no wavelength resolution (and thus cannot be used to unfold the distribution of energy from an X-ray source) it will provide a powerful tool in mapping out the structure of extended X-ray sources such as supernova remnants and with its high temporal resolution will be able to trace the variation of emission with time from objects such as X-ray flare stars and pulsars.

ROSAT also carries another smaller, soft X-ray telescope, called the Wide Field Camera (WFC), which is devoted entirely to studies of the extreme ultraviolet region of the spectrum. These lower energies cover the wavelength range 60 to 600 Å, and the British built WFC will carry out a simultaneous all-sky survey in conjunction with the hard X-ray telescope. This survey will be particularly exciting for extreme ultraviolet astronomers, since only thirteen non-Solar System sources have ever been observed between 100 and 1000 Å. The WFC, which was designed and built by a consortium of UK institutions led by Leicester University, consists of a 60 cm aperture grazing incidence Wolter-type telescope coupled to two identical curved microchannel plate detectors. After the six-month sky survey any one of eight specially fabricated thin film filters can be moved into the WFC telescope exit beam to define more precise wavelength passbands for a more detailed study of selected objects.

The ROSAT satellite, launched from the Kennedy Space Center in Florida on a Delta-II rocket in mid-1990, was placed into an orbit of 57° inclination and 600 km altitude. Initially, a two-month check-out phase was planned in which the scientific instruments were carefully powered up and put through some calibrational experiments. Immediately following this phase of the mission the six month all-sky survey began and on completion will be followed by the pointed observations of selected, interesting X-ray sources.

Command and control of the space-craft operations are being carried out by the German Space Operations Centre in Munich.

So, what will be in store for the X-ray astronomers using ROSAT? First, we can assume that in the hard X-ray sky survey some 100,000 new X-ray sources will be detected. In the extreme ultraviolet region, estimates range from 50 to 5000 new sources. The uncertainty in detections in this wavelength régime is due to the unknown distribution of hydrogen gas (which universally fills the space between the stars) within 150 light-years of the Sun. Even very small amounts of neutral hydrogen can absorb extreme ultraviolet radiation very efficiently and thus it is most likely that the WFC will only detect sources in the nearby interstellar medium.

The types of X-ray sources that both experiments will be able to study in the pointed observation phase of the mission will be extremely varied. For example, it is known that stars, like the planets, generate magnetic fields in their hot interiors by the motions of charged fluids called dynamos. Both X-ray and extreme ultraviolet emission has been observed in the coronæ (or rarefied outer atmospheres) of many late-type stars, indicating a link between stellar magnetic fields and coronal activity. ROSAT will be able to obtain new insights into the detailed mechanisms which produce this emission and may shed new light on current theories which appear to suggest that the X-rays are linked in some way to the rotation rate and chemical composition of these stars.

At the other end of the cosmological scale, X-rays are known to originate in many of those distant and enigmatic objects called quasars. Since hard X-rays are virtually unaffected by intergalactic absorption, it will be possible to observe quasars at great distances, and hence ROSAT will be able to look back into the very earliest times in the history of the Universe.

Closer to home in our own Milky Way galaxy, ROSAT will be able to study many of the rotating neutron stars which we call pulsars. These 20-km diameter, incredibly densely packed objects are the end-point of supernovæ explosions and are known to generate X-rays produced by the high temperature gas left over from the original cataclysmic supernova explosion. Some of these objects are termed 'binary pulsars' in which hot gas is pulled along a stellar wind from a normal, main sequence star on to a nearby compact companion neutron star. Very little of the gas actually falls on to the neutron star surface itself; instead most of it swirls around the neutron star, forming a disk of very hot gas called an accretion disk. This disk is at very high temperatures (in excess of several millions degrees) because of the immense gravitational forces being exerted on it by the neutron star. The most famous X-ray binary system of this type is Her X-1, in which the X-rays are observed in pulses with a regular period of 1.237 seconds. Unlike radio pulsars, the X-ray pulses from Her X-1 vanish completely for 6 hours every 1.7 days when the emitting neutron star is eclipsed from our view by its stellar companion.

Many X-ray sources are binary in nature, either having a neutron star companion or in the extreme case, a collapsed massive neutron star – or 'black hole'. The most likely candidate for a black hole is the object Cygnus X–1, which lies about 10,000 light-years away. The X-ray emitting system is thought to contain a hot, massive supergiant star which is losing its mass at a rate of about 10^{-9} Solar masses per year to a nearby object which is invisible to us at optical wavelengths. The X-ray emission from this system flickers rapidly at a rate of about one-thousandth of a second, indicating that the emitting region must be less than one-thousandth of a light-second in diameter (i.e. $<$ 300 km)! Calculations indicate that this very small companion is a condensed object with a mass of about eight Solar masses. This means that it is probably a black hole, since the theoretical limit for a neutron star mass is five Solar masses. It should be noted here that we are NOT seeing X-rays from the black hole itself, but from the superheated accretion disk of material that is swirling in close proximity to it.

ROSAT will also be able to detect and map out the distribution of X-ray emission from distant galaxies and clusters of galaxies. It is hoped that this information will help us understand the problem of 'dark matter' in the Universe. The existence of dark matter was first inferred about twenty years ago, when it was observed that the amount of matter needed to account for the gravitational effects in galactic clusters far exceeded the matter that was known to exist in the form of individual stars and galaxies. Although dark matter cannot be studied directly, it can be observed indirectly through its gravitational effects on other forms of matter. Very hot gas, which can only be seen in X-rays, has been observed in many large astronomical systems (such as galactic clusters) and it is thought that this gas is being held in the tight gravitational grip of dark matter. Hopefully, ROSAT will be able to map out the spatial structure of such gravitational fields which theory predicts are dependent on the temperature and mass of the hidden dark matter particles.

So far we have dealt with the more distant members of the Universe that the hard X-ray instrument on ROSAT will be more suited to detect. The WFC, operating in the extreme ultraviolet region, will be more parochial in its observations, its horizons being limited by the dense clouds of hydrogen gas that are known to exist in the interstellar medium beyond about 300 light years. One class of object that will be studied in great detail by the WFC will be white dwarf stars. In fact, the first non-Solar object to be detected in this wavelength region was a hot white dwarf star called HZ 43; an object only 180 light-years away being no larger than the Earth, weighing about the same as the Sun and having a temperature of 60,000 K! Such bizarre objects represent the end-points of evolution for stars similar to our own Sun, and hence should be quite numerous in the Galaxy. They are the exposed cores of stars which have shed their outer atmospheres after the red giant and planetary nebula stages of stellar evolution. They have stopped burning nuclear fuel and contain degenerate matter in which the electrons are packed so tightly that they cannot move freely in a random fashion. Eventually, over a period of a billion years or so, white dwarfs cool down from their high temperatures and end their lives as burnt-out black dwarfs. It is estimated that the WFC could detect as many as a thousand white dwarfs within 200 light-years of the Sun, and these observations will help in the understanding of the chemical and physical composition of their stellar atmospheres.

Thus it can be seen that the ROSAT mission will detect a wide variety of X-ray sources at distances ranging from as close as our Solar neighbourhood to the very edge of the observable Universe. ROSAT will certainly extend our knowledge of the hot phase of matter throughout the Universe and will most likely pose new problems for the next generation of X-ray space missions to solve. We have certainly come a long way in the century since Wilhelm Roentgen first discovered those unknown, or 'X' rays, in his small Earth-bound laboratory in Germany.

Tramps, Runaways, Tides, Streams and Cooling Flows:

THE STARS OF INTERGALACTIC SPACE

PAUL MURDIN

We live on a planet orbiting the Sun, a star in a galaxy. Our nearest neighbour star system, Proxima, is a mere four light-years away. Nearly all stars lie in galaxies, collections of stars which are separated from their neighbours by vast and almost unimaginable distances.

But intergalactic space is not empty. There are stars which course in the space between galaxies, rare exceptions to the rule that you only find stars in galaxies, intergalactic tramps, lonely stars experiencing the ultimate in separation – megaparsecs, not light-years. How did they get there?

Our Galaxy's massive halo

Travel, in your imagination, outwards from our Sun, in the plane of the Milky Way, towards the constellation of Taurus. At 3,000 light-years, pass beyond the Crab Nebula and exit from the dust, the nebulæ and the bright stars of the spiral arms of our Galaxy, penetrating into its thin halo.

At a distance of some 200,000 light-years the stars of the halo of our Galaxy are very sparse indeed. A few rare brighter stars in the halo are giants, caught in their quick evolution from Solar-type stars to white dwarfs. But most of the stars here are mere sparklers compared to the bright fireworks of the Solar neighbourhood, as well as few, and far between. Solar-type stars and redder, cooler stars are in the majority; the white dwarfs and neutron stars, most of them black, are difficult to see but perhaps very numerous.

There are indications from the ways that stars in galaxies move and experience the gravitational pull of others that spiral galaxies such as ours have haloes much more massive than the number of visible stars would make you believe. In this sense the mass of the haloes is 'missing'. Without these haloes, spiral patterns of galaxies would disintegrate quickly into chaos. The stars of the massive haloes are dark (because we do not see them) and they constitute one of the forms of the *missing matter*, material whose effects, via the pull of gravity, astronomers see, but of which directly they have no trace. Are these white dwarfs and neutron stars which we vaguely see in this imaginary journey the missing mass of our own Galaxy?

At a distance of 200,000 light-years we have almost left the Galaxy behind and are entering intergalactic space. At this distance the pull of our Galaxy is weak. At the edge of the Galaxy we can stop, in our imagination. Stars cannot stop. Some stars coast slowly past us, evaporating from our Galaxy, like molecules of water from a drying puddle of rain. Some of these stars slowly move ever outwards into intergalactic space, dark stars into darker space, almost invisible intergalactic tramps.

The Magellanic Stream

From our destination in the halo of our Galaxy look back to our Sun and to the centre of the Galaxy, lying beyond. The Galaxy looks thin and elongated – a flat disk like a frisbee, edge-on. A line of dust in the plane of the Galaxy cuts the disk of the Galaxy in two. The disk seems to thicken in the middle – here is the central bulge of our Galaxy, the transition zone between disk and halo, although no one knows if the bulge is a central condensation of the halo or, physically, a thickening of the disk.

Centred on the bulge is a swarm of globular clusters of millions of stars. Created soon after the initial formation of our Galaxy they orbit in elongated trajectories in and out through the central bulge. One globular cluster nearby to us hovers at the end of its elongated flight, poised (it seems for ever but in fact only for millions of years), ready to plunge again into the crowded nuclear bulge.

Below the plane of the Galaxy you can see its two satellite galaxies, the Large and the Small Magellanic Clouds. They are our Galaxy's nearest neighbours, less than 200,000 light-years from our Sun. At our back is the Andromeda Galaxy, M 31, the nearest twin to our own spiral galaxy: it is nearly ten times further from the Sun than the Magellanic Clouds.

From our new vantage point we can see that the 'Small' cloud is actually larger than the 'Large' cloud. The Small Magellanic Cloud seems small as viewed from Earth because it is long and thin and seen end on. From the vantage point which we have reached, we

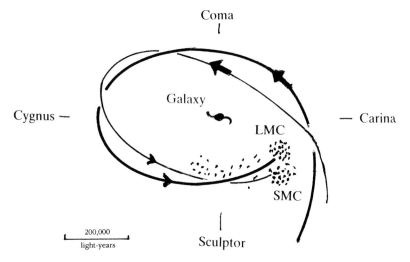

Figure 1. *The orbits of the two Magellanic Clouds and the origin of the Magellanic Stream. This diagram is a view of our Galaxy from a position in the galactic plane a long way off, in the direction of Taurus. The Small and the Large Magellanic Clouds (SMC and LMC respectively) orbit each other as they loop around our Galaxy, trailing a tail of hydrogen gas like meteoric dust from a comet.*

view its stick-like shape sideways on and can appreciate its full length. It has been elongated by its encounter with the Large Magellanic Cloud in orbit around the Galaxy. The two clouds are linked together like a double-star system, orbiting each other as they orbit together counter-clockwise around our Galaxy as seen from the point which we have reached in our imagination.

The two Magellanic Clouds came as close together, 200 million years ago, as they ever do – as close as 10,000 light-years. Their mutual gravitational attraction raised fierce tides on each other. The disturbance can be traced as the so-called 'wing' of the Small Magellanic Cloud, which, in the words of its discoverer, Harlow Shapley, is a 'large cloud of faint stars extending eastwards from the SMC to the LMC'. A bridge of hydrogen gas linked the two galaxies, torn from each. Stars formed from the hydrogen in the bridge, stars which have been discovered in the inter-Cloud link by Mike Irwin, Serge Demers and Bill Kunkel using the Automatic Plate-measuring Machine at the University of Cambridge to scan photographic plates taken by the UK Schmidt Telescope in Australia. These young stars extend all the way from the SMC to the western halo of the LMC – the stars belong to neither galaxy.

As well as the bridge which connects the two Clouds, a stream of hydrogen gas spilled from the two galaxies and now lies in an arch, 300,000 light-years long, spanning our Galaxy. In imagination we can see it in profile from our vantage point, trailing back from the two Clouds like the curved tail of a comet (Figure 1) and mapping the past orbit of the pair of satellite galaxies. This arch of gas is known as the *Magellanic Stream*.

So far the Magellanic Stream has been discovered only in the form of hydrogen gas, mapped by astronomers of the Southern Hemisphere, particularly Australia, together with other elements associated with hydrogen in space – calcium and sodium, for example. Fruitless searches, with the COSMOS automatic plate measuring machine at the Royal Observatory Edinburgh on deep photographs with the UK Schmidt Telescope in Australia for stars which could be members of the Magellanic Stream, have shown that the number of stars in the Magellanic Stream is not large. There are presumably *some* stars in this gas, possibly stars with planetary systems, whose inhabitants look up on to our own Galaxy from their position in the arch below, peering with fascination at our Galaxy's spiral arms, a whirlpool of light practically filling the hemisphere of their night sky at the appropriate seasons of the year.

Intergalactic Tides

The Magellanic Stream is not the only such intergalactic bridge. It contains few stars. But in other more extreme cases, it is possible to photograph stars in brighter bridges which span the space between galaxies which have passed close to each other (Figure 2). The stars have been stripped from their parent galaxy by the pull of the other. They lie in what appear to be threads, given fanciful names such as The Antennæ, the Mouse Tails. They appear to be long and thin, as the names imply, but the bridges are in fact the edges of sheets of stars viewed in perspective like a curved fan of water from a fountain. Sometimes the sheets are dense enough to show face on – the names of the disturbed galaxies indicate what the sheets look like: the Fly's Wing, the Seashell.

As the galaxies separate, the stars of these tidal bridges will disperse into a lonely existence in intergalactic space, some perhaps with planets, their inhabitants able to view the once-colliding galaxies, receding in opposite parts of the sky.

Figure 2. NGC 2992-3. The galaxies in this photo by David Malin form an interacting trio, with tides of stars pulled like toffee from each, forming bridges between two pairs. A disturbed erratic spiral arm breaks free from one galaxy on the far side of the interaction. © *1979 AAT Board.*

Runaway Stars

Individual stars may be shot from the galaxy in which they were born, and sent speeding into intergalactic space.

A star in orbit in a galaxy could encounter something else and be whipped into a high velocity orbit around it, propelled into intergalactic space like a missile from a sling-shot. Encounters with giant interstellar clouds might do this, or an encounter between a star and a heavy, double-star system. Astronomers can simulate such encounters in a computer and it seems that the latter are especially likely to eject the star with enough speed that it could escape our Galaxy.

Again, one member of a multiple star system could be ejected with galactic escape velocity from the system if one of the other members exploded as a supernova. Such high velocity stars are called *runaway stars*.

How would you recognize a runaway star when you saw one? One characteristic would be its high speed. Another would be that it would be a long way from its birthplace. At the present time stars are born mostly in the plane of our Galaxy since this is the region which contains the gas from which stars condense.

If young stars were found in the halo of our Galaxy above the plane, then until recently they would have been assumed to have been runaway stars. Astronomers at Queen's University Belfast have been studying stars which at first sight were of this kind but which have turned out not to be: their origins are even more mysterious. Francis Keenan, Philip Dufton and Paul Brown have been turning up examples of young massive stars well above the galactic plane which are so slowly moving that in their lifetime they could not have reached so high.

One such star, PG0832+676, whose nature the astronomers of Queen's University Belfast identified with the Isaac Newton Telescope on La Palma, lies 60,000 light-years above the galactic plane and is moving so slowly it cannot have been born in the Milky Way. It seems, however, to have been born out of normal galactic plane material, so the identifiers conjecture that gas is transported from the galactic plane into the halo first and the star was born out of it there.

How did the gas get there? Perhaps the vast explosions of supernovæ energize gas, and squirt it upwards from the plane in galactic fountains. Like the Magellanic Stream, the gas was ripped from its normal position and the stars then formed from it.

Cooling Flows

Another way of moving gas in intergalactic space is the so-called *cooling flow*. X-ray astronomers often detect X-rays from clusters of galaxies – not just from the galaxies themselves but from the intergalactic regions within the cluster. These X-rays come from hot gas. Although the gas is generally distributed throughout the cluster, it often peaks on one central galaxy. In other cases (about half), clusters have no central galaxy and the X-ray emission is not peaked.

There is as much mass in the X-ray emitting region as in the stars of the cluster. The gas is heated by the thermal motions of the galaxies in the cluster – they move back and forth through the cluster stirring it up, and the gas gets hot as a consequence. It cools centrally and the cooling time is less than the age of the cluster. Therefore the density in the centre must increase in order to support the rest of the gas; therefore there must be an inflow of material towards the middle in order to boost the density.

This is the 'cooling flow'. The actual cooling can be seen in the range of temperatures in the X-ray spectra of the clusters – put all the clusters in a sequence of decreasing temperature and you have the equivalent of a series of snapshots in the evolution of a single cooling cluster.

Since half of the known clusters of galaxies have the peaky X-ray emission, cooling flows are a common process and must be long lived.

The rate of cooling is high; 50 to 200 (or even 500) Solar masses per year is a range for the amount of cooling material in a cluster. Some individual galaxies are increasing in mass at a rate of a few Solar masses per year. A 'few' stars may seem very little compared to the 100,000 million stars in a galaxy, but if the process lasts for the lifetime of the cluster (20,000 million years), as appears to be the case, a galaxy can gain as much material by this process as it had originally.

What happens to the cluster material which flows in towards a central galaxy? What does it look like? Does it in fact form stars? Astronomers are not sure. The cooling flow may form gaseous filaments – there are some central galaxies in clusters which have such filaments and they may have been formed in this way. Perseus A (the galaxy NGC 1275) is one such example.

The cooling flow may create a dark halo around the galaxy. The halo could be in the form of low-mass stars, too dim to see individually. (They must be Solar type or fainter.) If so, the build up of the dense part of the cooling flow effectively disappears from view. Evidently the cooling flow does not form bright stars in the same way that stars form in our own Galaxy, because the haloes around the central galaxies in cooling flows are hard to see. If the cooling flow around the galaxy Perseus A were forming bright stars at the rate of 200 Solar masses per year (as is calculated) it would be, at 300 million light-years distance, a binocular object with many bright stars. It is not.

In fact in only one case is there direct evidence that dim stars are condensing in the cooling flow. A faint red glow surrounds the central galaxy in the cluster 1E1111.9-3754 (Figure 3). This cluster is one which was identified by a group of Italian astronomers from

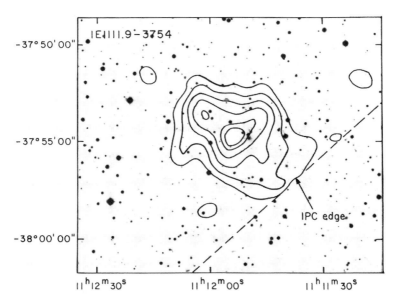

Figure 3. The contours represent the X-ray emission from the cluster 1E1111.9-3754 as viewed by the Einstein Observatory satellite's IPC instrument. The contours show a general increase of X-ray emission towards a central area. The contours are overlaid on a negative picture from the UK Schmidt Sky Atlas (black stars and galaxies). Near the centre of the contours, just on the second contour from the centre, is a fuzzy image, which is GREG, the Giant Red Envelope Galaxy. The contours map the cooling flow and GREG's envelope of red stars condensed from it, according to Johnstone and Fabian. (Reproduced by courtesy of the Italian astronomers named in the text.)

Milan and Bologna to be a source of X-ray emission seen by the Einstein Observatory X-ray satellite.

In 1987 the group (D. Maccagni, B. Garilli, I. M. Gioia, T. Maccacaro, G. Vettolani and A. Wolter) used the new instrument known as EFOSC at the European Southern Observatory in Chile, which can make images of stars and galaxies, and obtain their spectra very efficiently by feeding the light from several objects at once into the spectrograph incorporated in the instrument. They discovered that the central galaxy in the cluster had an unusually large diffuse halo of reddish light. They nicknamed the galaxy GREG – giant red envelope galaxy.

According to Cambridge astronomers Roderick Johnstone and Andy Fabian, the halo in GREG represents stars which formed from the cooling flow of the cluster, stars born and bred there in the intergalactic space between the galaxies.

Recent Novæ

JOHN ISLES

Novæ or 'new stars' were the first objects in the heavens, outside our own Solar System, in which change was noticed, and they have played an important part in the history of astronomy since its first beginnings. The early records, mainly by observers in the Far East, do not always clearly distinguish between comets and novæ, but it was probably the appearance of a genuine nova in the constellation Scorpius in 134 BC that prompted Hipparchus to compile the first extensive catalogue of naked-eye stars, in order that later astronomers should be able to detect further changes. According to one theory, the Star of Bethlehem may have been a nova of 4 BC in Aquila, recorded also in China and Korea. It was Tycho Brahe's observations of the nova of 1572 (which today we would call a supernova) that exploded the Aristotelian doctrine of the immutability of the stellar heavens, and opened the way to new speculations about the nature of the Universe.

We now know that novæ are close binary stars containing a normal or 'main-sequence' star, somewhat cooler than our own Sun, and a hot white dwarf star. White dwarfs represent a closing stage of stellar evolution, in which the star has exhausted its nuclear fuel as well as its gravitational energy, and its remnant has shrunk to about the size of the Earth, although it can contain a mass greater than that of the Sun. Its matter is crushed into a degenerate form with a density up to 100 million times that of water, and the star can shine only by radiating its remaining heat into space as it cools down to become a non-luminous 'black dwarf'.

In nova systems, the main-sequence secondary star is losing mass in a stream that flows in the direction of its white-dwarf companion, but the material does not usually land directly on the surface of the hot primary, because it has too much angular momentum or 'spin'. Instead, it forms a bright 'accretion disk' around the hot star. Binary stars that have this structure are called 'cataclysmic variables', whether or not nova outbursts have yet been seen in them.

Nova outbursts are due to the nuclear burning to helium, near the surface of the white dwarf star, of the hydrogen-rich material it has accumulated from its companion. This takes place in a sudden 'thermonuclear runaway' when a critical mass, density and temperature have been reached. The enormous amount of energy released – as much as our Sun radiates in 1,000 years – blows a large mass of hot gas into space, causing the light emitted by the binary system to increase dramatically.

A very energetic fast nova, such as V1500 Cygni which erupted in 1975, can rise by up to 19 magnitudes, or 40 million times in apparent brightness, in as little as 24 hours, before fading back to minimum over several months. Most novæ are not quite so spectacular, and there are several different ways in which the outburst may develop. Astronomers distinguish two main classes, the fast novæ, in which the initial fade by three magnitudes takes 100 days or less, and the slow novæ, in which the same stage takes 150 days or more. But of the 200-odd novæ that have been studied, no two are quite the same.

The outbursts of normal or 'classical' novæ are thought to recur at intervals of tens of thousands of years. In some objects, however, more than one outburst has been seen, at intervals that range from eight to eighty years. These 'recurrent novæ' are a mixed bag of objects that in some cases resemble the Z Andromedæ or 'symbiotic' stars, which have red-giant secondary components, or the U Geminorum stars or 'dwarf novæ', in which the outbursts are not due to a thermonuclear runaway but are the pulsed release, in the form of light and heat, of gravitational energy in the accretion disk. The outbursts of recurrent novæ are generally briefer than those of classical novæ, and the observations necessary to establish their true nature are not always available, but some of them certainly do seem to undergo true thermonuclear events.

Another class of objects resembling the novæ in their outbursts, but with a different structure, includes the X-ray novæ. Here the compact companion is a neutron star, or even a black hole. Neutron stars comprise matter in an even denser state than white dwarfs, with electrons and protons crushed together to form neutrons. Black holes are objects in which the matter has been literally crushed to a point. Their gravitational fields are so strong that even light cannot escape from them, so that we have no means of observing them directly. The presence of black holes in certain X-ray binaries has been inferred from estimates of their masses, which are greater than can be supported by the structure of a neutron star; but alternative interpretations can be made of the observations. The outbursts of X-ray novæ recur at similar intervals to those seen in the ordinary recurrent novæ.

Although our understanding of novæ has improved greatly in recent years, they remain very important to astronomers as celestial laboratories in which high-energy phenomena can be observed that are well beyond what can be produced on Earth. Amateur astronomers contribute by providing detailed coverage of the brightness in the course of the outbursts, and during the intervals between outbursts when secondary variations are often seen. Most nova discoveries are also made by amateurs; in fact they almost monopolize the field.

Discovering novæ

Table 1, below, lists the nova discoveries in our Galaxy, and its two satellite galaxies the Large and Small Magellanic Clouds (LMC

TABLE 1
Nova discoveries, 1985–89

Nova	R.A. (2000.0)		Declination		Mag. at discovery	Discoverer
	h	m	deg.	min.		
RS Oph 1985	17	50.2	−06	43	6.8	W. Morrison, USA
V960 Sco 1985	17	56.6	−31	49	10.5	W. Liller, Chile
V1819 Cyg 1986	19	54.7	+35	42	9.4	M. Wakuda, Japan
V842 Cen 1986	14	36.0	−57	38	5.6	R. McNaught, Australia
OS And 1986	23	12.2	+47	28	8.0	M. Suzuki, Japan
SMC 1986	00	36.9	−72	05	10.0	R. McNaught, Australia
V827 Her 1987	18	43.9	+15	19	8.5	M. Sugano and M. Honda, Japan
BW Cir 1987	13	58.2	−64	44	16.9	Ginga satellite
U Sco 1987	16	22.5	−17	53	10.8	D. Overbeek, South Africa
V4135 Sgr 1987	17	59.8	−32	16	10.4	R. McNaught, Australia
V394 CrA 1987	18	00.4	−39	01	7.5	W. Liller, Chile
LMC 1987	05	23.9	−70	01	11.9	G. Garradd, Australia
QV Vul 1987	19	04.7	+21	46	7.0	K. Beckmann and P. Collins, USA
PQ And 1988	02	29.6	+40	03	10.1	D. McAdam, England
LMC 1988 No 1	05	35.6	−70	21	11.4	G. Garradd, Australia
V2214 Oph 1988	17	12.0	−29	37	8.5	M. Wakuda, Japan
QZ Vul 1988	20	02.8	+25	15	17.5	Ginga satellite
LMC 1988 No 2	05	08.1	−68	58	11.3	G. Garradd, Australia
V404 Cyg 1989	20	24.2	+33	52	12.8	Ginga satellite
V745 Sco 1989	17	55.4	−33	15	9.7	W. Liller, Chile
Sco 1989	17	51.9	−32	32	10.0	W. Liller, Chile
Sct 1989	18	49.7	−05	58	10.5	P. Wild, Switzerland

and SMC), that were reported in the period 1985 to 1989. Novæ are named in the same way as other variable stars. The first variable in a constellation is called R; the next S, then T, and so on up to Z. Then double letters are used: RR to RZ, SS to SZ, and so on up to ZZ; then AA to AZ, BB to BZ, and so on up to QZ (except that the letter J is never used).

This system, invented in the nineteenth century before photographic methods enormously multiplied the numbers of discoveries, provides for up to 334 variable stars in each constellation. After that, numbers are used: V335, V336, etc. In the constellation Sagittarius, which includes rich star fields in the direction of the centre of our Galaxy, over 4,000 variables are now known; the latest nova in this part of the sky, discovered by Robert McNaught in 1987, is called V4135 Sagittarii. Novæ in other galaxies, such as the SMC and LMC, are not included in this naming system, and the last two novæ found in 1989 had not received official designations up to the time of writing.

Also given in Table 1 are the approximate positions of each nova, in terms of right ascension and declination for epoch 2000.0; the magnitude of each object at the time of discovery (or, for X-ray novæ, the first optical detection); and the discoverer's name. Most novæ are near maximum when found, but some continue to rise; the brightest one in this five-year interval was V842 Cen of 1986, which reached magnitude 4.6.

About thirty nova outbursts are thought to occur in our Galaxy each year, but most of them are missed. They may be distant objects, too faint to stand a chance of detection, or they may be obscured by interstellar dust clouds; but the statistics of discoveries indicate that our record even of novæ that reach naked-eye brightness is very incomplete: 1987 was exceptional with as many as seven novæ, but most years yield three or four discoveries. Only a few dozen novæ have been well observed, so it is very useful work to search for more.

The best place to look is near the plane of our Galaxy. One search method, employed very successfully by George Alcock of Peterborough, England, is to sweep the star fields of the Milky Way with binoculars every clear night, memorizing the star patterns and keeping alert to possible intruders. This work yielded him four nova discoveries between 1967 and 1976, as well as several comets.

More recently, amateurs have had much success with photographic patrols. Of the 22 nova outbursts found during 1985–89, as many as 16 were discovered in this way. An ordinary 35-mm camera can be used: preferably one with an interchangeable lens facility and a 'B' setting, and without an electronic shutter that might cause the battery to run down during an exposure. With a 50-mm lens of about f/2 (25-mm aperture) and a fast film such as Tri-X, star trails below eighth magnitude can be recorded in unguided exposures of 30 seconds, while in dark skies a guided exposure of 2–3 minutes will show stars to magnitude 10. With a 135-mm f/2.8 lens (48-mm aperture), stars below magnitude 10 can be recorded in an unguided exposure of 10 seconds, covering of course a smaller area of sky. Apart from novæ, by-products of patrols with such simple equipment have included a crop of bright new variable stars and even occasional comets, such as Comet McNaught 1987b$_1$.

The 16 novæ found in photographic patrols in 1985–89 included 14 new objects, and second outbursts in two objects now reclassified as recurrent novæ: V394 CrA, previously seen in 1949, and V745 Sco, whose earlier maximum was in 1937. The 6 nova outbursts found in the same period by different methods were the joint discovery of Nova QV Vul 1987, by two amateurs searching visually; those of the previously known recurrent novæ RS Oph and U Sco, stars that are regularly monitored visually by amateurs; and 3 X-ray novæ found by the Japanese Ginga satellite, which were only subsequently identified optically (by an amateur in one case).

In addition to the listed events during this period, three possible novæ in the Andromeda Galaxy were reported from photographs by one amateur astronomer in the USA, J. T. Bryan, and a nova of 1983 in Sagittarius was found by another in Japan, M. Wakuda, upon re-examining his earlier photographs. The fact that several observers have multiple discoveries to their credit indicates that there is still much scope for additional outbursts to be found by newcomers to the search for novæ.

Novæ in 1989

The year began quietly for nova observers with no discoveries during the first four months. On May 22, F. Makino Sagamihara of the Ginga satellite team reported an X-ray nova in Cygnus, at a position close to that of Nova V404 Cyg of 1938. Martin Mobberley of Chelmsford, England, made the first optical detection with a photograph on May 26 which confirmed the identity of the two objects. It rose to magnitude 11.9 on May 28, by when it had become, after our Sun, the strongest X-ray source in the sky, with an intensity seventeen times that of the Crab Nebula. Spectra of V404 Cyg resembled those of the X-ray recurrent nova V616 Mon, in which the compact component is a black hole candidate. The new star faded more rapidly than V616 Mon, however, and in July it was at about magnitude 15.

A brightening of the old nova GK Per 1901 was detected in July by Bill Worraker, England. This was the tenth mini-outburst to be seen in this star since 1966. It rose to magnitude 10.5 in August, but by the end of September it had fallen back to its normal magnitude 13.

Bill Liller, observing from Vina del Mar, Chile, reported two novæ in Scorpius from his photographic patrol work. The first, found on July 24, proved to be a second outburst of Nova V745 Sco 1937. The second, found during the total lunar eclipse of August 17, was a completely new object just one degree north-west of V745 Sco. Both stars faded rapidly, and the second would almost certainly have been missed altogether but for Liller's observation: a classic illustration of the importance of letting no opportunity go to waste.

Finally, on September 20, P. Wild of Berne University found a 10.5 magnitude nova near the Wild Duck open cluster (M11) at the northern edge of the Scutum Star Cloud. Nova Sct 1989 proved to be a slow nova, oscillating between magnitudes 9.7 and 12 up to the end of the year. The Scutum Star Cloud has yielded several nova discoveries over the years, including George Alcock's Nova V368 Sct 1970, two degrees south-west of M11, and Nova V373 Sct 1975, another discovery by Wild, a degree and a half south-east of the cluster.

The coming years are sure to see exciting developments in the study of novæ, in which amateurs will continue to make an important contribution.

Comet Austin – What Went Wrong?

HAROLD B. RIDLEY

Comet Austin has been a most disappointing object. It is not the first comet to be so – the memory of the infamous Comet Kohoutek of 1973 still rankles, and even the illustrious Halley's Comet made its least favourable return on record and was a mediocre object for Northern Hemisphere observers. On the other hand, comets have been known to flare up and be much brighter than expected. Although the majority of comets are well-behaved and predictable, a fair number of them refuse to conform to the expected pattern: Comet Austin is a good example of this maverick tendency.

Rodney Austin, a New Zealand amateur astronomer, discovered his third comet on 6 December, 1989, and it was given the designation $1989c_1$ to indicate the year and order of discovery and to distinguish it from the other two comets that bear his name. Both his previous discoveries were quite nice comets, though not spectacular, so the present runner seemed to come from a good stable.

The first priority when a new comet is discovered is to determine its orbit, which can then be used to predict its future position and brightness. In this case the orbit showed that the comet would pass comparatively close to the Sun at perihelion (closest point to the Sun) and on its way out would approach the Earth fairly closely. All this was to the good, for the closer a comet passes to the Sun and the Earth the brighter it will be. Although rather badly placed for observation during the perihelion stage, it would be more favourably situated subsequently.

All the signs and calculations indicated that Comet Austin would be a fine object, perhaps reaching first magnitude, equal in brightness to the brightest naked-eye stars, and that it would very likely sport a long bright tail. A photograph taken at La Silla Observatory, high up in the Chilean Andes, was very encouraging; it showed two streamers of gas 2° long, and a stump of dust-tail. Observations by the IUE satellite indicated that the dust-production rate, important for the development of a strong tail, was greater than that of

Halley's Comet in similar circumstances. The comet was looking good, and all seemed well. What went wrong?

To answer that question it is necessary to understand the origin of the light that reaches us from the comet, and the manner in which the amount of light received depends on the distances of the comet from the Sun and the Earth, and on the composition of the cometary material.

The light that we receive from a comet originates in two different ways. First, there is simply sunlight reflected from the solid components of the comet: the nucleus, or central body, and the dust particles in the coma (head) and the tail if there is one. This follows the well-known inverse-square law – double the distance and the light is reduced to one-quarter of its previous value; treble it and the light will fall to one-ninth. Conversely, halve the distance and the light increases four-fold, and so on. All very straightforward, but it does depend on the amount of dust present as well as on the size of the nucleus, and the former can vary unexpectedly. In the case of Comet Austin the dust-production rate fell considerably in March, and with it the chance of a very bright comet and a good tail.

The second source of a comet's light depends on a mechanism similar to that used in our familiar tubular fluorescent lamps. Heat from the Sun causes the frozen gases of the nucleus to evaporate (strictly, to sublime) and these in turn carry away any dust particles mixed in with the ices. A dusty gaseous atmosphere is generated around the nucleus, and this is known as the coma, together with the nucleus forming the head of the comet. The atoms and molecules of these gases are then energized (excited) by ultraviolet light from the Sun; we on Earth are shielded from this radiation by the ozone layer of our own atmosphere. The excited particles later calm down and shed some of their excess energy in the form of visible light. The amount of light emitted depends on the nature of the gases, e.g., cyanogen (CN), carbon monoxide (CO), water vapour (H_2O) and on the intensity of the ultraviolet radiation received. The effect of Solar distance varies in a complicated way, which entails an element of uncertainty in our predictions.

Many of the atoms and molecules in the coma absorb so much energy that their outermost electrons are stripped off, i.e., they become ionized, with a net positive electric charge, and some of the molecules are split into separate ions. All around the comet are the outwardly-moving high-speed charged particles from the Sun, the Solar Wind, and these, in conjunction with the lines of force of the interplanetary magnetic field, accelerate the cometary ions radially away from the Sun, and compress them into narrow streams, forming the ion tail, often referred to as the gas-tail or plasma-tail.

The solid dust-grains are repelled much more slowly by ordinary light-pressure from the Sun, and tend to lag behind the head, giving the dust-tail a curved form rather like the stream of water from a moving hosepipe. A comet may have either or both types of tail, and sometimes neither is strong enough to be visible, depending on the composition of the material and the distance from the Sun.

All these facts can now be put together to explain the basis of our predictions of the brightness and form of a given comet. A standard formula is used in most cases, as follows:

$$m = m_o + 5 \log\triangle + n \log r$$

In this formula, m is the observed magnitude of the comet, $\triangle$ is the distance from the Earth and r is the distance from the Sun. Distances are expressed in Astronomical Units, 1 AU being the mean distance of the Earth from the Sun. Magnitudes are measured on a logarithmic scale, the smaller the number the brighter the object. The second term of the equation simply embodies the inverse-square law, but the third term gives the relation between comet brightness and Solar distance. This varies from comet to comet, and often at different times for a given comet, usually changing to some extent after perihelion passage.

Since the logarithm of 1 is zero, when $\triangle$ and r are both equal to 1, we are left with m_o, which is known as the absolute magnitude of the comet, i.e., its brightness when the Sun, Earth and comet respectively occupy the corners of an equilateral triangle each side of which is 1 AU.

The values of m_o and n are critical for the forecasting of the comet's brightness, and can only be determined from a series of observations over a reasonable time interval. At first, we assume n = 10 for want of a more precise figure. The early observations of Comet Austin indicated that $m_o = 5$, and this, together with the assumed n = 10, led to our over-optimistic expectations. Later observations have shown $m_o = 8$, and n = 7.5 approximately, leading to our dashed hopes.

As to why the comet misled us in the early stages there is no categorical answer, but we may possibly get a clue from the nature of its orbit. When a comet is first discovered and only a few positions are available we have to assume that the orbit is parabolic – i.e., an open curve on the borderline between a closed ellipse and an even more open hyperbola. Later, with a longer arc to work with, the calculations can be refined and the precise orbital form derived. In the case of Comet Austin the orbit turns out to be very slightly hyperbolic. An object in such an orbit must have come in from a very great distance, unless it passed close to one of the giant planets, which this comet did not.

It is thought that beyond the furthest planet, Pluto, and extending about halfway to the nearest stars, there is a shell or halo of comets, invisible at that distance. This swarm of comets is known as the Oort Cloud, after the Dutch astronomer who first proposed the hypothesis. These comets are moving very slowly and will creep around in near-interstellar space for perhaps billions of years – in fact, we believe them to be the most primitive material remaining from the original nebula from which the Solar System evolved – which is one reason for their great interest to astronomers.

Sooner or later some of these comets will be disturbed (perturbed) by a passing star and either lost from the Sun's feeble hold or directed inwards towards it. The traffic density of passing stars is extremely low, so there must be vast numbers of comets to account for the few that we see coming in every year.

Comet Austin, therefore, is probably a 'new' comet, making its first approach to the Sun after aeons in the outer darkness and near-absolute-zero cold of distant space. Perhaps, during its long sojourn in these conditions, or maybe in the final stages of its first formation, it accreted a thin surface layer of highly volatile materials with a considerable dust content – possibly dust grains coated with frozen gases. As soon as the comet approached the Sun within the orbit of Jupiter, solar heating would sublime the very volatile surface layer together with its entrained dust particles, giving rise to the misleading brightness and dustiness shown by the early observations. This is one possible explanation for our unfulfilled initial hopes.

A factor that was not given sufficient weight at first was the effect of the adverse viewing circumstances that would prevail during the brighter phases of the apparition. The observed brightness of a comet is very sensitive to the darkness and lucidity of the sky. These are dependent on the angular separation (elongation) of the comet from the Sun, and on the altitude or height above the horizon. When the altitude is low the light from the comet has to travel through an increased atmospheric path, particularly of the lower levels which are more heavily contaminated with water vapour, dust and other pollutants, and a great deal of the light is scattered and absorbed. The effect is especially severe on extended objects such as nebulæ and comets; the point-source stars are less affected. Near the horizon, the outer coma and tail of a comet will disappear unless they are exceptionally bright, and the comet will look like a fuzzy star, much fainter than it would otherwise be.

The elongation of a comet from the Sun is critical for its visibility. This angle depends on the lengths of the sides of the Sun–Earth–Comet triangle (Figure 1) and for a comet with small perihelion distance is always rather narrow when the comet is at its brightest. If the angle is less than about 30° it will be impossible to see the comet in a really dark sky; there will always be more or less twilight degrading the contrast. From the end of March until mid-April, the elongation of Comet Austin was around 20°, making it difficult to see, low in the bright evening twilight. As the comet moved into the morning sky the elongation gradually increased reaching a comfortable 70° in mid-May.

Two other factors influencing the perceived brightness of a comet are the incidence of moonlight and the effect of local lighting. The latter is rapidly degrading the conditions for all astronomical observations, but is particularly baneful for diffuse objects such as comets. Observers in cities or large towns have little hope of seeing

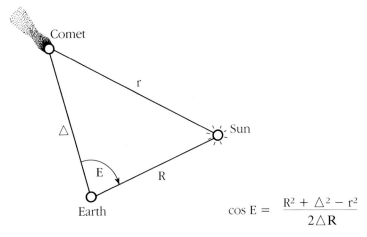

$$\cos E = \frac{R^2 + \triangle^2 - r^2}{2\triangle R}$$

Figure 1. The Sun–Earth–Comet triangle. E = elongation.

comets well, and even the countryside suffers to an increasing extent from light-pollution. In the case of Comet Austin, the Moon was full at the time of perihelion, and followed the comet into the morning sky, so the best conditions did not prevail until the last week of April.

When a comet has passed perihelion and departs from the Sun, its intrinsic brightness fades, but in the present case the lie of the orbit was such that after perihelion the comet approached the Earth, appearing larger and brighter than it would otherwise have done, and the magnitude held steady through May, when the coma diameter swelled to two-thirds the apparent diameter of the full Moon, though the tail became practically invisible. In the first week of June, the comet came into line with the Sun and the Earth so that the tail was strongly foreshortened and subsequently the comet moved rapidly southwards and faded quickly as it headed out on its unregretted departure for interstellar space.

Comet Austin failed to live up to our expectations because of its deceptive early brightness and latterly through the hindrance of poor observing circumstances. Thought to reach first magnitude with a tail 10°–20° long, it barely achieved fourth magnitude and the tail was thin, faint and only at most 3°–4° in length. Even at that, it was better than the average run-of-the-mill comet, as the excellent photograph by Denis Buczynski (Figure 2) shows.

One final question remains: if the behaviour of comets is so chancy, why not simply wait and see what happens, rather than risk raising false hopes? Many professional astronomers who do not routinely observe comets will do so in the case of a very bright one, and in any case time is needed to formulate programmes and arrange equipment. Above all, telescope time must be booked (usually months ahead) or swaps arranged. Even amateurs may wish to arrange holidays to coincide with the best observing time. If a bright comet appears without warning, the interested public will complain: 'You might have told us!' So even though there will doubtless be other Kohouteks and Austins, the alert must be given, even if the notes of caution that go with it are ignored.

Figure 2. Comet Austin, photographed on 27 April 1990, 01h. 58m.–02h. 04m., by Denis Buczynski and G. Marsh at Conder Brow Observatory.

Some Interesting Variable Stars

The following stars are of interest for many reasons. The positions are given for epoch 2000. Of course, the periods and ranges of many variables are not constant from one cycle to another.

Star	R.A. h	m	Declination deg.	min.	Range	Type	Period days	Spectrum
R Andromedæ	00	24.0	+38	35	5.8–14.9	Mira	409	S
W Andromedæ	02	17.6	+44	18	6.7–14.6	Mira	396	S
U Antliæ	10	35.2	−39	34	5.7– 6.8	Irregular	–	N
θ Apodis	14	05.3	−76	48	6.4– 8.6	Semi-reg.	119	M
R Aquarii	23	43.8	−15	17	5.8–12.4	Symbiotic	387	M+Pec
T Aquarii	20	49.9	−05	09	7.2–14.2	Mira	202	M
R Aquilæ	19	06.4	+08	14	5.5–12.0	Mira	284	M
V Aquilæ	19	04.4	−05	41	6.6– 8.4	Semi-reg.	353	N
η Aquilæ	19	52.5	+01	00	3.5– 4.4	Cepheid	7.2	F–G
U Aræ	17	53.6	−51	41	7.7–14.1	Mira	225	M
R Arietis	02	16.1	+25	03	7.4–13.7	Mira	187	M
U Arietis	03	11.0	+14	48	7.2–15.2	Mira	371	M
ε Aurigæ	05	02.0	+43	49	2.9– 3.8	Eclipsing	9892	F
R Aurigæ	05	17.3	+53	35	6.7–13.9	Mira	457	M
R Boötis	14	37.2	+26	44	6.2–13.1	Mira	223	M
W Boötis	14	43.4	+26	32	4.7– 5.4	Semi-reg.	450	M
X Camelopard	04	45.7	+75	06	7.4–14.2	Mira	144	K–M
R Cancri	08	16.6	+11	44	6.1–11.8	Mira	362	M
X Cancri	08	55.4	+17	14	5.6– 7.5	Semi-reg.	195	N
R Canum Ven.	13	49.0	+39	33	6.5–12.9	Mira	329	M
R Canis Maj.	07	19.5	−16	24	5.7– 6.3	Algol	1.2	F
S Canis Min.	07	32.7	+08	19	6.6–13.2	Mira	333	M
R Carinæ	09	32.2	−62	47	3.9–10.5	Mira	309	M
S Carinæ	10	09.4	−61	33	4.5– 9.9	Mira	150	K–M
ZZ Carinæ	09	45.2	−62	30	3.3– 4.2	Cepheid	35.5	F–K
η Carinæ	10	45.1	−59	41	−0.8– 7.9	Irregular	–	Pec.
γ Cassiopeiæ	00	56.7	+60	43	1.6– 3.3	Irregular	–	B
ρ Cassiopeiæ	23	54.4	+58	30	4.1– 6.2	?	–	F–K
R Cassiopeiæ	23	58.4	+51	24	4.7–13.5	Mira	431	M
W Cassiopeiæ	00	54.9	+58	34	7.8–12.5	Mira	406	N
S Cassiopeiæ	01	19.7	+72	37	7.9–16.1	Mira	612	S
R Centauri	14	16.6	−59	55	5.3–11.8	Mira	546	M
S Centauri	12	24.6	−49	26	6.0– 7.0	Semi-reg.	65	N
T Centauri	13	41.8	−33	36	5.5– 9.0	Semi-reg.	60	K–M
δ Cephei	22	29.2	+58	25	3.5– 4.4	Cepheid	5.4	F–G
μ Cephei	21	43.5	+58	47	3.4– 5.1	Irregular?	–	M
S Cephei	21	35.2	+78	37	7.4–12.9	Mira	487	N
ο Ceti	02	19.3	−02	59	1.7–10.1	Mira	332	M
W Ceti	00	02.1	−14	41	7.1–14.8	Mira	361	S
R Chamæleontis	08	21.8	−76	21	7.5–14.2	Mira	335	M
T Columbæ	05	19.3	−33	42	6.6–12.7	Mira	226	M
R Comæ Ber.	12	04.0	+18	49	7.1–14.6	Mira	363	M
R Coronæ Bor.	15	48.6	+28	09	5.7–15	Irregular	–	Fp
W Coronæ Bor.	16	15.4	+37	48	7.8–14.3	Mira	238	M
R Corvi	12	19.6	−19	15	6.7–14.4	Mira	317	M

Star	R.A. h	m	Declination deg.	min.	Range	Type	Period days	Spectrum
R Crucis	12	23.6	−61	38	6.4– 7.2	Cepheid	6.7	F
R Cygni	19	36.8	+50	12	6.1–14.2	Mira	426	M
χ Cygni	19	50.6	+32	55	3.3–14.2	Mira	407	S
U Cygni	20	19.6	+47	54	5.9–12.1	Mira	462	N
W Cygni	21	36.0	+45	22	5.0– 7.6	Semi-reg.	126	M
SS Cygni	21	42.7	+43	35	8.4–12.4	Dwarf nova	±50	A–G
R Delphini	20	14.9	+09	05	7.6–13.8	Mira	285	M
U Delphini	20	45.5	+18	05	7.6– 8.9	Semi-reg.?	110?	M
EU Delphini	20	37.9	+18	16	5.8– 6.9	Semi-reg.?	59?	M
β Doradûs	05	33.6	−62	29	3.7– 4.1	Cepheid	9.8	F–G
R Draconis	16	32.7	+66	45	6.7–13.0	Mira	245	M
T Eridani	03	55.2	−24	02	7.4–13.2	Mira	252	M
R Fornacis	02	29.3	−26	06	7.5–13.0	Mira	388	N
η Geminorum	06	14.9	+22	30	3.1– 4.2	Semi-reg.	±233	M
ξ Geminorum	07	04.1	+20	34	3.7– 4.1	Cepheid	10.2	F–G
R Geminorum	07	07.4	+22	42	6.0–14.0	Mira	370	S
U Geminorum	07	55.1	+22	00	8.2–14.9	Dwarf nova	±103	M+WD
S Gruis	22	26.1	−48	26	6.0–15.0	Mira	401	M
α Herculis	17	14.6	+14	23	3.0– 4.0	Semi-reg.	±100	M
S Herculis	17	17.3	+35	06	4.6– 5.3	Beta Lyræ	2.1	B+B
U Herculis	16	25.8	+18	54	6.5–13.4	Mira	406	M
R Hydræ	13	29.7	−23	17	4.0–10.0	Mira	390	M
U Hydræ	10	37.6	−13	23	4.8– 5.8	Semi-reg.	450	N
VW Hydri	04	09.1	−71	18	8.4–14.4	Dwarf nova	100	M
R Leonis	09	47.6	+11	25	4.4–11.3	Mira	312	M
R Leonis Min.	09	45.6	+34	31	6.3–13.2	Mira	372	M
R Leporis	04	59.6	−14	48	5.5–11.7	Mira	432	N
δ Libræ	15	01.1	−08	31	4.9– 5.9	Algol	2.3	B
Y Libræ	15	11.7	−06	01	7.6–14.7	Mira	275	M
R Lyncis	07	01.3	+55	20	7.2–14.5	Mira	379	S
β Lyræ	18	50.1	+33	22	3.3– 4.3	Beta Lyræ	12.9	B+A
R Lyræ	18	55.3	+43	57	3.9– 5.0	Semi-reg.	46	M
RR Lyræ	19	25.5	+42	47	7.1– 8.1	RR Lyræ	0.6	A–F
U Microscopii	20	29.2	−40	25	7.0–14.4	Mira	334	M
U Monocerotis	07	30.8	−09	47	6.1– 8.1	RV Tauri	92	F–K
S Monocerotis	06	41.0	+09	54	4 – 5?	Irregular	–	07
T Normæ	15	44.1	−54	59	6.2–13.6	Mira	243	M
R Octantis	05	26.1	−86	23	6.4–13.2	Mira	406	M
S Octantis	18	08.7	−86	48	7.3–14.0	Mira	259	M
RS Ophiuchi	17	50.2	−06	43	5.3–12.3	Recurrent nova	–	O+M
X Ophiuchi	18	38.3	+08	50	5.9– 9.2	Mira	334	M+K
α Orionis	05	55.2	+07	24	0.1– 0.9	Semi-reg. ±	2110	M
U Orionis	05	55.8	+20	10	4.8–12.6	Mira	372	M
W Orionis	05	05.4	+01	11	5.9– 7.7	Semi-reg.	212	N
ϰ Pavonis	18	56.9	−67	14	3.9– 4.7	W Virginis	9.1	F
S Pavonis	19	55.2	−59	12	6.6–10.4	Semi-reg.	386	M
β Pegasi	23	03.8	+28	05	2.3– 2.8	Semi-reg.	38	M
R Pegasi	23	06.8	+10	33	6.9–13.8	Mira	378	M
β Persei	03	08.2	+40	57	2.2– 3.4	Algol	2.9	B+G
ϱ Persei	03	05.2	+38	50	3 – 4	Semi-reg.	33to55	M
X Persei	03	55.4	+31	03	6 – 7	Irreg. (X-ray)	–	09.5
ζ Phœnicis	01	08.4	−55	15	3.9– 4.4	Algol	1.7	B+B
R Pictoris	04	46.2	−49	15	6.7–10.0	Semi-reg.	164	M
L² Puppis	07	13.5	−44	39	2.6– 6.2	Semi-reg.	140	M
T Pyxidis	09	04.7	−32	23	6.3–14.0	Recurrent nova	–	Q
U Sagittæ	19	18.8	+19	37	6.6– 9.2	Algol	3.4	B–K
WZ Sagittæ	20	07.6	+17	42	7.0–15.5	Recurrent nova	–	Q
RR Sagittarii	19	55.9	−29	11	5.6–14.0	Mira	335	M
RT Scorpii	17	03.5	−36	55	7.0–16.0	Mira	449	M
RY Sagittarii	19	16.5	−33	31	6.0–15	R Coronæ	–	Gp
S Sculptoris	00	15.4	−32	03	5.5–13.6	Mira	365	M

191

Star	R.A.		Declination		Range	Type	Period	Spectrum
	h	*m*	*deg.*	*min.*			*days*	
R Scuti	18	47.5	−05	42	4.4– 8.2	RV Tauri	140	G–K
R Serpentis	15	50.7	+15	08	5.1–14.4	Mira	356	M
S Serpentis	15	21.7	+14	19	7.0–14.1	Mira	369	M
λ Tauri	04	00.7	+12	29	3.3– 3.8	Algol	3.9	B+A
T Tauri	04	22.0	+19	32	8.4–13.5	T Tauri	–	G–K
SU Tauri	05	49.1	+19	04	9.1–16.0	R Coronæ	–	Gp
R Trianguli	02	37.0	+34	16	5.4–12.6	Mira	266	M
R Ursæ Major.	10	44.6	+58	47	6.7–13.4	Mira	302	M
T Ursæ Major.	12	36.4	+59	29	6.6–13.4	Mira	256	M
U Ursæ Minor.	14	17.3	+66	48	7.4–12.7	Mira	326	M
X Virginis	12	01.9	+09	04	7.3–11.2	?	–	F
SS Virginis	12	25.3	+00	48	6.0– 9.6	Mira	355	N
R Virginis	12	38.5	+06	59	6.0–12.1	Mira	146	M
S Virginis	13	33.0	−07	12	6.3–13.2	Mira	377	M
R Vulpeculæ	21	04.4	+23	49	7.0–14.3	Mira	136	M
Z Vulpeculæ	19	21.7	+25	34	7.4– 9.2	Algol	2.5	B+A

Mira Stars: maxima and minima, 1991

JOHN ISLES

Below are given predicted dates of maxima and minima for Mira stars on the programme of the BAA VSS, together with (usually) the *mean* range (p = photographic, otherwise visual), period (P), and fraction of the period taken in rising from minimum (m) to maximum (M) for each star. All dates are only approximate.

Star	Range		Period	$(M-m)/P$	Max.	Min.
	M	m	d			
R And	6.9	14.3	409	0.38	Aug. 23	Mar. 21
W And	7.4	13.7	396	0.42	—	Aug. 8
RW And	8.7	14.8	430	0.36	—	Aug. 12
R Aql	6.1	11.5	284	0.42	Oct. 2	June 4
V Cam	9.9	15.4	522	0.31	Dec. 26	Aug. 17
X Cam	8.1	12.6	144	0.49	Jan. 17, June 10, Nov. 1	Mar. 31, Aug. 22
SU Cnc*	12.0p	16p	187	0.43	July 4	Apr. 15, Nov. 19
U CVn*	8.8p	12.5p	346	0.39	Feb. 24	Sep. 23
RT CVn*	12.0p	16.0p	254	0.45	Apr. 19, Dec. 29	Sep. 6
S Cas	9.7	14.8	612	0.43	—	Sep. 6
T Cas	7.9	11.9	445	0.56	Dec. 10	Apr. 5
o Cet	3.4	9.3	332	0.38	Aug. 27	Apr. 23
R Com	8.5	14.2	363	0.38	Dec. 10	July 25
S CrB	7.3	12.9	360	0.35	Nov. 18	July 15
V CrB	7.5	11.0	358	0.41	June 6	Jan. 10
W CrB	8.5	13.5	238	0.45	Aug. 1	Apr. 16, Dec. 10
R Cyg	7.5	13.9	426	0.35	July 23	Feb. 24
S Cyg	10.3	16.0	323	0.50	Mar. 4	Aug. 12
V Cyg	9.1	12.8	421	0.46	—	July 20
Chi Cyg	5.2	13.4	408	0.41	Feb. 4	Oct. 3
T Dra	9.6	12.3	422	0.44	Nov. 3	May 28
RU Her	8.0	13.7	485	0.43	Feb. 7	Nov. 10

Star	Range		Period	$(M-m)/P$	Max.	Min.
	M	m	d			
SS Her	9.2	12.4	107	0.48	Mar. 14, June 29, Oct. 14	Jan. 23, May 9, Aug. 24, Dec. 9
R Hya	4.5	9.5	389	0.49	Dec. 16	June 8
SU Lac*	11.3p	16p	302	0.40	Sep. 1	May 3
RS Leo*	10.7p	16.0p	208	0.31	Mar. 29, Oct. 23	Jan. 24, Aug. 20
W Lyn*	7.5	14.0	295	0.47	Sep. 10	Apr. 24
X Lyn*	9.5	16	321	0.43	Nov. 12	June 27
X Oph	6.8	8.8	329	0.53	May 10	Oct. 12
U Ori	6.3	12.0	368	0.38	Dec. 13	July 26
R Ser	6.9	13.4	356	0.41	Apr. 11	Nov. 7
T UMa	7.7	12.9	257	0.41	June 20	Mar. 7, Nov. 19

*extreme range is given.

Some Interesting Double Stars

R. W. ARGYLE

Name	Magnitudes	Separation in seconds of arc	Position angle, degrees	Remarks
Gamma Andromedæ	2.3, 5.0	9.4	064	Yellow, blue. B is again double
Zeta Aquarii	4.3, 4.5	1.9	217	Slowly widening.
Gamma Arietis	4.8, 4.8	7.8	000	Very easy. Both white.
Theta Aurigæ	2.6, 7.1	3.5	313	Stiff test for 3-in.
Delta Boötis	3.5, 8.7	105	079	Fixed.
Epsilon Boötis	2.5, 4.9	2.8	335	Yellow, blue. Fine pair.
Zeta Cancri	5.6, 6.2	5.8	085	A again double.
Iota Cancri	4.2, 6.6	31	307	Easy. Yellow, blue.
Alpha Canum Ven.	2.9, 5.5	19.6	228	Easy. Yellow, bluish.
Alpha Capricorni	3.6, 4.2	379	291	Naked-eye pair.
Eta Cassiopeiæ	3.4, 7.5	12.5	312	Easy. Creamy, bluish.
Beta Cephei	3.2, 7.9	14	250	Easy with a 3-in.
Delta Cephei	var, 7.5	41	192	Very easy.
Alpha Centauri	0.0, 1.2	19.7	214	Very easy. Period 80 years.
Xi Cephei	4.4, 6.5	6.3	270	White, blue.
Gamma Ceti	3.5, 7.3	2.9	294	Not too easy.
Alpha Circini	3.2, 8.6	15.7	230	PA slowly decreasing.
Zeta Corona Bor.	5.1, 6.0	6.3	305	PA slowly increasing.
Delta Corvi	3.0, 9.2	24	214	Easy with a 3-in.
Alpha Crucis	1.4, 1.9	4.2	114	Third star in a low power field.
Gamma Crucis	1.6, 6.7	124	024	Third star in a low power field.
Beta Cygni	3.1, 5.1	34.5	055	Glorious. Yellow, blue.
61 Cygni	5.2, 6.0	30	148	Nearby binary. Period 722 years.
Gamma Delphini	4.5, 5.5	9.6	268	Easy. Yellowish, greenish.
Nu Draconis	4.9, 4.9	62	312	Naked eye pair.
Alpha Geminorum	1.9, 2.9	3.0	77	Widening. Visible with a 3-in.
Delta Geminorum	3.5, 8.2	6.5	120	Not too easy.
Alpha Herculis	var, 5.4	4.6	106	Red, green.
Delta Herculis	3.1, 8.2	9.8	272	Optical pair. Distance increasing.
Zeta Herculis	2.9, 5.5	1.6	084	Fine, rapid binary. Period 34 years.
Gamma Leonis	2.2, 3.5	4.4	123	Binary, 619 years.
Alpha Lyræ	0.0, 9.5	71	180	Optical pair. B is faint.

Name	Magnitudes	Separation in seconds of arc	Position angle, degrees	Remarks
Epsilon[1] Lyr	5.0, 6.1	2.6	356	Quadruple system. Both
Epsilon[2] Lyr	5.2, 5.5	2.2	093	pairs visible in a 3-in.
Zeta Lyræ	4.3, 5.9	44	149	Fixed. Easy double.
70 Ophiuchi	4.2, 6.0	1.5	224	Rapid motion.
Beta Orionis	0.1, 6.8	9.5	202	Can be split with a 3-in.
Iota Orionis	2.8, 6.9	11.8	141	Enmeshed in nebulosity.
Theta Orionis	6.7, 7.9	8.7	032	Trapezium in M42.
	5.1, 6.7	13.4	061	
Sigma Orionis	4.0, 10.3	11.4	238	Quintuple. A is a
	6.5, 7.5	30.1	231	close double.
Zeta Orionis	1.9, 4.0	2.4	162	Can be split in 3-in.
Eta Persei	3.8, 8.5	28.5	300	Yellow, bluish.
Beta Phœnicis	4.0, 4.2	1.5	324	Slowly widening.
Beta Piscis Aust.	4.4, 7.9	30.4	172	Optical pair. Fixed.
Alpha Piscium	4.2, 5.1	1.9	278	Binary, 933 years.
Kappa Puppis	4.5, 4.7	9.8	318	Both white.
Alpha Scorpii	1.2, 5.4	3.0	275	Red, green.
Nu Scorpii	4.3, 6.4	42	336	Both again double.
Theta Serpentis	4.5, 5.4	22.3	103	Fixed. Very easy.
Alpha Tauri	0.9, 11.1	131	032	Wide, but B very faint in small telescopes.
Beta Tucanæ	4.4, 4.8	27.1	170	Both again double.
Zeta Ursæ Majoris	2.3, 4.0	14.4	151	Very easy. Naked eye pair with Alcor.
xi Ursæ Majoris	4.3, 4.8	1.3	060	Binary, 60 years. Closing. Needs a 4-in.
Gamma Virginis	3.5, 3.5	3.0	287	Binary, 171 years. Closing.
Theta Virginis	4.4, 9.4	7.1	343	Not too easy.
Gamma Volantis	3.9, 5.8	13.8	299	Very slow binary.

Some Interesting Nebulæ and Clusters

Object	R.A.		Dec.		Remarks
	h	m			
M.31 Andromedæ	00	40.7	+41	05	Great Galaxy, visible to naked eye.
H.VIII 78 Cassiopeiæ	00	41.3	+61	36	Fine cluster, between Gamma and Kappa Cassiopeiæ.
M.33 Trianguli	01	31.8	+30	28	Spiral. Difficult with small apertures.
H.VI 33–4 Persei	02	18.3	+56	59	Double cluster; Sword-handle.
△142 Doradûs	05	39.1	−69	09	Looped nebula round 30 Doradûs. Naked-eye. In Large Cloud of Magellan.
M.1 Tauri	05	32.3	+22	00	Crab Nebula, near Zeta Tauri.
M.42 Orionis	05	33.4	−05	24	Great Nebula. Contains the famous Trapezium, Theta Orionis.
M.35 Geminorum	06	06.5	+24	21	Open cluster near Eta Geminorum.
H.VII 2 Monocerotis	06	30.7	+04	53	Open cluster, just visible to naked eye.
M.41 Canis Majoris	06	45.5	−20	42	Open cluster, just visible to naked eye.
M.47 Puppis	07	34.3	−14	22	Mag. 5,2. Loose cluster.
H.IV 64 Puppis	07	39.6	−18	05	Bright planetary in rich neighbourhood.
M.46 Puppis	07	39.5	−14	42	Open cluster.
M.44 Cancri	08	38	+20	07	Præsepe. Open cluster near Delta Cancri. Visible to naked eye.
M.97 Ursæ Majoris	11	12.6	+55	13	Owl Nebula, diameter 3'. Planetary.
Kappa Crucis	12	50.7	−60	05	'Jewel Box'; open cluster, with stars of contrasting colours.
M.3 Can. Ven.	13	40.6	+28	34	Bright globular.
Omega Centauri	13	23.7	−47	03	Finest of all globulars. Easy with naked eye.
M.80 Scorpii	16	14.9	−22	53	Globular, between Antares and Beta Scorpionis.
M.4 Scorpii	16	21.5	−26	26	Open cluster close to Antares.
M.13 Herculis	16	40	+36	31	Globular. Just visible to naked eye.
M.92 Herculis	16	16.1	+43	11	Globular. Between Iota and Eta Herculis.
M.6 Scorpii	17	36.8	−32	11	Open cluster; naked eye.
M.7 Scorpii	17	50.6	−34	48	Very bright open cluster; naked eye.
M.23 Sagittarii	17	54.8	−19	01	Open cluster nearly 50' in diameter.
H.IV 37 Draconis	17	58.6	+66	38	Bright Planetary.
M.8 Sagittarii	18	01.4	−24	23	Lagoon Nebula. Gaseous. Just visible with naked eye.
NGC 6572 Ophiuchi	18	10.9	+06	50	Bright planetary, between Beta Ophiuchi and Zeta Aquilæ.
M.17 Sagittarii	18	18.8	−16	12	Omega Nebula. Gaseous. Large and bright.
M.11 Scuti	18	49.0	−06	19	Wild Duck. Bright open cluster.
M.57 Lyræ	18	52.6	+32	59	Ring Nebula. Brightest of planetaries.
M.27 Vulpeculæ	19	58.1	+22	37	Dumb-bell Nebula, near Gamma Sagittæ.
H.IV 1 Aquarii	21	02.1	−11	31	Bright planetary near Nu Aquarii.
M.15 Pegasi	21	28.3	+12	01	Bright globular, near Epsilon Pegasi.
M.39 Cygni	21	31.0	+48	17	Open cluster between Deneb and Alpha Lacertæ. Well seen with low powers.

Our Contributors

Dr David Allen needs no introduction; he continues his work at the Siding Spring Observatory in New South Wales, and has been making a special study of the supernova in the Large Cloud of Magellan.

Professor A. P. Fairall is one of the leading astronomers at the University of Cape Town. In addition to his theoretical research he is very active in the popularization of astronomy, and is one of the main lecturers at the new Cape Town Planetarium.

Dr Allan Chapman is a world authority upon the history of science. He is Senior Tutor at the Centre for Medieval and Renaissance Studies at Oxford.

Dr Barry Welsh, who gained his doctorate from University College, London, in 1978, now works at the Space Sciences Laboratory of the University of California, Berkeley, where he is involved as a calibration scientist on NASA's Extreme Ultra-violet Explorer project. His present interests lie in mapping the gas content of the Local Interstellar Medium and in the development of new instrumentation for use in the soft X-ray region.

Dr Paul Murdin, O.B.E., is one of our most regular and valued contributors, and needs no introduction. In addition to his major theoretical and observational contributions to astronomy, he is an energetic popularizer, writer and broadcaster. He is Deputy Director of the Royal Greenwich Observatory, Cambridge.

John Isles lives in Cyprus. His main interest in astronomy concerns variable stars, and he directs the Variable Star Sections of both the British Astronomical Association and the Junior Astronomical Society.

Harold Ridley is one of our most senior and experienced observers of comets, and has been active in this field for many years. His comet photographs are known throughout the world.

The William Herschel Society maintains the museum now established at 19 New King Street, Bath – the only surviving Herschel house. It also undertakes activities of various kinds. New members would be welcome; those interested are asked to contact Dr L. Hilliard at 2 Lambridge, London Road, Bath.

Astronomical Societies in Great Britain

British Astronomical Association
Assistant Secretary: Burlington House, Piccadilly, London W1V 9AG.
Meetings: Lecture Hall of Scientific Societies, Civil Service Commission Building, 23 Savile Row, London W1. Last Wednesday each month (Oct.–June). 1700 hrs and some Saturday afternoons.

Association for Astronomy Education
Secretary: Bob Kibble, 34 Ackland Crescent, Denmark Hill, London SE5 8EQ.

Astronomical Society of Wales
Secretary: John Minopoli, 12 Gwendoline Street, Port Talbot, West Glamorgan.

Federation of Astronomical Societies
Secretary: Mrs Christine Sheldon, Whitehaven, Lower Moor, Pershore, Worcs.

Junior Astronomical Society
Secretary: M. Ratcliffe, 36 Fairway, Keyworth, Nottingham.
Meetings: Central Library, Theobalds Road, London WC1. Last Saturday Jan., April, July, Oct. 2.30 p.m.

Junior Astronomical Society of Ireland
Secretary: K. Nolan, 5 St Patrick's Crescent, Rathcoole, Co. Dublin.
Meetings: The Royal Dublin Society, Ballsbridge, Dublin 4. Monthly.

Aberdeen and District Astronomical Society
Secretary: Stephen Graham, 25 Davidson Place, Northfield, Aberdeen.
Meetings: Robert Gordon's Institute of Technology, St Andrew's Street, Aberdeen. Friday 7.30 p.m.

Altrincham and District Astronomical Society
Secretary: Colin Henshaw, 10 Delamore Road, Gatley, Cheadle, Cheshire.
Meetings: Public Library, Timperley. 1st Friday of each month, 7.30 p.m.

Astra Astronomy Section
Secretary: Ian Downie, 151 Sword Street, Glasgow G31.
Meetings: Public Library, Airdrie. Weekly.

Aylesbury Astronomical Society
Secretary: Peter Biswell, 6 Northfield Road, Aylesbury, Bucks.

Bassettlaw Astronomical Society
Secretary: P. R. Stanley, 28 Festival Avenue, Harworth, nr. Doncaster.
Meetings: Farr Community Hall, Chapel Walk, Westgate, Worksop, Notts. Tuesday fortnightly, 7.30 p.m.

Batley & Spenborough Astronomical Society
Secretary: A. Burrows, 4 Norwood Drive, Batley, West Yorks.
Meetings: Milner K. Ford Observatory, Wilton Park, Batley. Every Thursday, 7.30 p.m.

Bedford Astronomical Society
Secretary: D. Eagle, 24 Copthorne Close, Oakley, Bedford.
Meetings: Bedford School, Burnaby Rd, Bedford. Last Tuesday each month.

Bingham & Brookes Space Organization
Secretary: N. Bingham, 15 Hickmore's Lane, Lindfield, W. Sussex.

Birmingham Astronomical Society
Secretary: P. Truelove, 58 Taylor Road, King's Heath, Birmingham.
Meetings: Room 261, University of Aston, last Tuesday each month, Sept. to May.

Blackpool & District Astronomical Society
Secretary: J. L. Crossley, 24 Fernleigh Close, Bispham, Blackpool, Lancs.

Bolton Astronomical Society
Secretary: Peter Miskiw, 9 Hedley Street, Bolton.

Border Astronomical Society
Secretary: David Pettit, 14 Shap Grove, Carlisle, Cumbria.

Boston Astronomers
Secretary: B. Tongue, South View, Fen Road, Stickford, Boston.
Meetings: Details from the Secretary.

Bradford Astronomical Society
Secretary: John Schofield, Briar Lea, Bromley Road, Bingley, W. Yorks.
Meetings: Eccleshill Library, Bradford 2. Monday fortnightly (with occasional variations).

Braintree, Halstead & District Astronomical Society
Secretary: Heather Reeder, The Knoll, St Peters in the Field, Braintree, Essex.
Meetings: St Peter's Church Hall, St Peter's Road, Braintree, Essex. 3rd Thursday each month, 8 p.m.

Bridgend Amateur Astronomical Society
Secretary: J. M. Pugsley, 32 Hoel Fawr, Broadlands, North Cornelly, Bridgend.
Meetings: G.P. Room, Recreation Centre, Bridgend, 1st and 3rd Friday monthly, 7.30 p.m.

Bridgwater Astronomical Society
Secretary: W. L. Buckland, 104 Polden Street, Bridgwater, Somerset.
Meetings: Room D10, Bridgwater College, Bath Road Centre, Bridgwater. 2nd Wednesday each month, Sept.–June.
Brighton Astronomical Society
Secretary: Mrs B. C. Smith, Flat 2, 23 Albany Villas, Hove, Sussex BN3 2RS.
Meetings: Preston Tennis Club, Preston Drive, Brighton. Weekly, Tuesdays.
Bristol Astronomical Society
Secretary: Y. A. Sage, 33 Mackie Avenue, Filton, Bristol.
Meetings: Royal Fort (Rm G44), Bristol University. Every Friday each month, Sept.–May. Fortnightly, June–August.
Cambridge Astronomical Association
Secretary: Dr F. W. Murphy, 98 High Street, Harlton, Cambridge.
Meetings: The Friends Meeting House, Jesus Lane, Cambridge. 3rd Friday each month, 8 p.m.
Cardiff Astronomical Society
Secretary: D. W. S. Powell, 1 Tal-y-Bont Road, Ely, Cardiff.
Meeting Place: Room 230, Dept. Law, University College, Museum Avenue, Cardiff. Alternate Thursdays, 8 p.m.
Chelmsford and District Astronomical Society
Secretary: Miss C. C. Puddick, 6 Walpole Walk, Rayleigh, Essex.
Meetings: Sandon House School, Sandon, near Chelmsford. 2nd and last Monday of month. 7.45 p.m.
Chester Astronomical Society
Secretary: Mrs S. Brooks, 39 Halton Road, Great Sutton, South Wirral.
Meetings: Southview Community Centre, Southview Road, Chester. Last Monday each month except Aug. and Dec., 7.30 p.m.
Chester Society of Natural Science Literature and Art
Secretary: Paul Braid, 'White Wing', 38 Bryn Avenue, Old Colwyn, Colwyn Bay, Clwyd.
Meetings: Grosvenor Museum, Chester. Fortnightly.
Chesterfield Astronomical Society
Secretary: P. Lisewski, 148 Old Hall Road, Brampton, Chesterfield.
Meetings: Barnet Observatory, Newbold. Each Friday.
Clacton & District Astronomical Society
Secretary: C. L. Haskell, 105 London Road, Clacton-on-Sea, Essex.
Cleethorpes & District Astronomical Society
Secretary: Peter Rea, 1 Rosina Grove North, Grimsby.
Meetings: Beacon Hill Observatory, Cleethorpes. 1st Wednesday each month.
Cleveland & Darlington Astronomical Society
Secretary: Neil Haggath, 5 Fountains Cresc., Eston, Middlesbrough, Cleveland.
Meetings: Monthly, usually second Friday. Sept. to June. Stockton Sixth Form College, Bishopton Road West, Stockton-on-Tees.
Colchester Amateur Astronomers
Secretary: F. Kelly, 'Middleton', Church Road, Elmstead Market, Colchester, Essex.
Meetings: William Loveless Hall, High Street, Wivenhoe. Friday evenings. Fortnightly.
Cotswold Astronomical Society
Secretary: A. Ireland, 8 Merestone Drive, The Park, Cheltenham, Gloucs.
Meetings: Fortnightly in Cheltenham or Gloucester.
Coventry & Warwicks Astronomical Society
Secretary: Alan Hancocks, 33 Gainford Rise, Binley, Coventry.
Meetings: Coventry Technical College. 1st Friday each month, Sept.–June.
Crawley Astronomical Society
Secretary: G. Cowley, 67 Climpixy Road, Ifield, Crawley, Sussex.
Meetings: Crawley College of Further Education. Monthly Oct.–June.
Crayford Manor House Astronomical Society
Secretary: R. H. Chambers, Manor House Centre, Crayford, Kent.
Meetings: Manor House Centre, Crayford. Monthly during term-time.
Croydon Astronomical Society
Secretary: N. Fisher, 5 Dagmar Road, London SE25 6HZ.
Meetings: Lanfranc High School, Mitcham Rd, Croydon. Alternate Fridays, 7.45 p.m.
Derby & District Astronomical Society
Secretary: Jane D. Kirk, 7 Cromwell Avenue, Findern, Derby.
Meetings: At home of Secretary. First and third Friday each month, 7.30 p.m.
Doncaster Astronomical Society
Secretary: J. A. Day, 297 Lonsdale Avenue, Intake, Doncaster.
Meetings: Fridays, weekly.

Dundee Astronomical Society
Secretary: G. Young, 37 Polepark Road, Dundee, Angus.
Meetings: Mills Observatory, Balgay Park, Dundee. First Friday each month, 7.30 p.m. Sept.–April.

Easington and District Astronomical Society
Secretary: T. Bradley, 52 Jameson Road, Hartlepool, Co. Durham.
Meetings: Easington Comprehensive School, Easington Colliery. Every third Thursday throughout the year, 7.30 p.m.

Eastbourne Astronomical Society
Secretary: D. C. Gates, Apple Tree Cottage, Stunts Green, Hurstmonceux, East Sussex.
Meetings: St Aiden's Church Hall, Seaside, Eastbourne. Monthly (except July and August).

East Lancashire Astronomical Society
Secretary: D. Chadwick, 16 Worston Lane, Great Harwood, Blackburn BB6 7TH.
Meetings: As arranged. Monthly.

Astronomical Society of Edinburgh
Secretary: R. G. Fenoulhet, 7 Greenend Gardens, Edinburgh EH17 7QB.
Meetings: City Observatory, Calton Hill, Edinburgh. Monthly.

Edinburgh University Astronomical Society
Secretary: c/o Dept. of Astronomy, Royal Observatory, Blackford Hill, Edinburgh.

Ewell Astronomical Society
Secretary: Ron W. Johnson, 19 Elm Way, Ewell, Surrey.
Meetings: 1st Friday of each month.

Exeter Astronomical Society
Secretary: Miss J. Corey, 5 Egham Avenue, Topsham Road, Exeter.
Meetings: The Meeting Room Wynards, Magdalen Street, Exeter. 1st Thursday of month.

Farnham Astronomical Society
Secretary: Laurence Anslow, 14 Wellington Lane, Farnham, Surrey.
Meetings: Church House, Union Road, Farnham. 2nd Monday each month, 7.45 p.m.

Fitzharry's Astronomical Society (Oxford & District)
Secretary: J. Fathers, 94 Freelands Road, Oxford.
Meetings: Monthly, Sept.–May.

Furness Astronomical Society
Secretary: A. Thompson, 52 Ocean Road, Walney Island, Barrow-in-Furness, Cumbria.
Meetings: St Mary's Church Centre, Dalton-in-Furness. 2nd Saturday in month, 7.30 p.m. No August meeting.

Fylde Astronomical Society
Secretary: 28 Belvedere Road, Thornton, Lancs.
Meetings: Stanley Hall, Rossendale Ave. South. 1st Wednesday each month.

Astronomical Society of Glasgow
Secretary: Malcolm Kennedy, 32 Cedar Road, Cumbernauld, Glasgow.
Meetings: University of Strathclyde, George St., Glasgow. 3rd Thursday each month, Sept.–April.

Grimsby Astronomical Society
Secretary: R. Williams, 14 Richmond Close, Grimsby, South Humberside.
Meetings: Secretary's home. 2nd Thursday each month, 7.30 p.m.

Guernsey: La Société Guernesiaise Astronomy Section
Secretary: David Le Conte, Belle Etoile, Rue de Hamel, Castel, Guernsey.
Meetings: Monthly.

Guildford Association Society
Secretary: Mrs Joan Prosser, 115 Farnham Road, Guildford, Surrey.
Meetings: Guildford Institute, Ward Street, Guildford. 1st Thursday each month. Sept.–June, 7.30 p.m.

Gwynedd Astronomical Society
Secretary: P. J. Curtis, Ael-y-bryn, Malltraeth St Newborough, Anglesey, Gwynedd.
Meetings: Physics Lecture Room, Bangor University. 1st Thursday each month, 7.30 p.m.

The Hampshire Astronomical Group
Secretary: R. Dodd, 1 Conifer Close, Cowplain, Portsmouth.
Meetings: Clanfield Observatory. Each Friday, 7.30 p.m.

Astronomical Society of Haringey
Secretary: Wally Baker, 58 Stirling Road, Wood Green, London N22.
Meetings: The Hall of the Good Shepherd, Berwick Road, Wood Green. 3rd Wednesday each month, 8 p.m.

Harrogate Astronomical Society
Secretary: J. N. Eagin, 23 Crowberry Drive, Harrogate, North Yorks.

Heart of England Astronomical Society
Secretary: R. D. Januszewski, 24 Emsworth Grove, Kings Heath, Birmingham.
Meetings: Chelmsley Wood Library. Last Thursday each month.

Hebden Bridge Literary & Scientific Society, Astronomical Section
Secretary: F. Parker, 48 Caldene Avenue, Mytholmroyd, Hebden Bridge, West Yorkshire.
Herschel Astronomical Society
Secretary: Dr A. K. Welch, Tumbleweed, The Common, Winchmore-Hill, Amersham, Bucks.
Meetings: Trinity Church Annex, Windsor Road, Slough. Fortnightly, Friday.
Howards Astronomy Club
Secretary: H. Ilett, 22 St Georges Avenue, Warblington, Havant, Hants.
Meetings: To be notified.
Huddersfield Astronomical and Philosophical Society
Secretary (Assistant): M. Armitage, 37 Frederick Street, Crossland Moor, Huddersfield.
Meetings: 4A Railway Street, Huddersfield. Every Friday, 7.30 p.m.
Hull and East Riding Astronomical Society
Secretary: J. I. Booth, 3 Lynngarth Ave., Cottingham, North Humberside.
Meetings: Ferens Recreation Centre, Chanterlands Avenue, Hull. 1st Friday each month, Oct.–April, 7.30 p.m.
Ilkeston & District Astronomical Society
Secretary: Trevor Smith, 129 Heanor Road, Smalley, Derbyshire.
Meetings: The Friends Meeting Room, Ilkeston Museum, Ilkeston. 2nd Tuesday monthly, 7.30 p.m.
Ipswich, Orwell Astronomical Society
Secretary: R. Gooding, 168 Ashcroft Road, Ipswich.
Meetings: Orwell Park Observatory, Nacton, Ipswich. Wednesdays 8 p.m.
Irish Astronomical Association
Secretary: Michael Duffy, 26 Ballymurphy Road, Belfast, Northern Ireland.
Meetings: Room 315, Ashby Institute, Stranmills Road, Belfast. Fortnightly. Wednesdays, Sept.–April, 7.30 p.m.
Irish Astronomical Society
Secretary: c/o PO Box 2547, Dublin 15, Eire.
Isle of Wight Astronomical Society
Secretary: J. W. Feakins, 1 Hilltop Cottages, High Street, Freshwater, Isle of Wight.
Meetings: Unitarian Church Hall, Newport, Isle of Wight. Monthly.
Keele Astronomical Society
Secretary: Miss Caterina Callus, University of Keele, Keele, Staffs.
Meetings: As arranged during term time.
King's Lynn Amateur Astronomical Association
Secretary: P. Twynman, 17 Poplar Avenue, RAF Marham, King's Lynn.
Meetings: As arranged.
Lancaster and Morecambe Astronomical Society
Secretary: Miss E. Haygarth, 27 Coulston Road, Bowerham, Lancaster.
Meetings: Midland Hotel, Morecambe. 1st Wednesday each month except January. 7.30 p.m.
Lancaster University Astronomical Society
Secretary: c/o. Students Union, Alexandra Square, University of Lancaster.
Meetings: As arranged.
Laymans Astronomical Society
Secretary: John Evans, 10 Arkwright Walk, The Meadows, Nottingham.
Meetings: The Popular, Bath Street, Ilkeston, Derbyshire. Monthly.
Leeds Astronomical Society
Secretary: A. J. Higgins, 23 Montagu Place, Leeds LS8 2RQ.
Meetings: Lecture Room, City Museum Library, The Headrow, Leeds.
Leicester Astronomical Society
Secretary: Dereck Brown, 64 Grange Drive, Glen Parva, Leicester.
Meetings: Judgemeadow Community College, Marydene Drive, Evington, Leicester. 2nd and 4th Tuesdays each month, 7.30 p.m.
Limerick Astronomy Club
Secretary: Tony O'Hanlon, 54 Ballycannon Heights, Meelick, Co. Clare, Eire.
Meetings: Mechanics Institute, Hartstonge, Limerick, Eire. Monthly (except June and August), 8 p.m.
Lincoln Astronomical Society
Secretary: G. Winstanley, 36 Cambridge Drive, Washingborough, Lincoln.
Meetings: The Lecture Hall, off Westcliffe Street, Lincoln. 1st Tuesday each month.
Liverpool Astronomical Society
Secretary: Martin Sugget.
Meetings: City Museum, Liverpool. Monthly.
Loughton Astronomical Society
Meetings: Loughton Hall, Rectory Lane, Loughton, Essex. Thursdays 8 p.m.

Lowestoft and Great Yarmouth Regional Astronomers (LYRA) Society
Secretary: S. Briggs, 65 Stubbs Wood, Gunton Park, Lowestoft, Suffolk.
Meetings: Committee Room No. 30, Lowestoft College of F.E., St Peter's Street, Lowestoft. 3rd Thursday, Sept.–May (weather permitting on Corton Cliff site), 7.15 p.m.

Luton & District Astronomical Society
Secretary: D. Childs, 6 Greenways, Stopsley, Luton.
Meetings: Luton College of Higher Education, Park Square, Luton. Second and last Friday each month, 7.30 p.m.

Lytham St Annes Astronomical Association
Secretary: K. J. Porter, 141 Blackpool Road, Ansdell, Lytham St Annes, Lancs.
Meetings: College of Further Education, Clifton Drive S., Lytham St Annes. 2nd Wednesday monthly Oct.–June.

Maidenhead Astronomical Society
Secretary: c/o Chairman, Peter Hunt, Hightrees, Holyport Road, Bray, Berks.
Meetings: Library. Monthly (except July) 1st Friday.

Maidstone Astronomical Society
Secretary: N. O. Harris, 19 Greenside, High Hadden, Ashford, Kent.
Meetings: Nettlestead Village Hall, 1st Tuesday in month except July and Aug. 7.30 p.m.

Mansfield and Sutton Astronomical Society
Secretary: G. W. Shepherd, Sherwood Observatory, Coxmoor Road, Sutton-in-Ashfield, Notts.
Meetings: Sherwood Observatory, Oakmoor Road. Last Tuesday each month.

Mexborough and Swinton Astronomical Society
Secretary: Mark R. Benton, 61 The Lea, Swinton, Mexborough, Yorks.
Meetings: Methodist Hall, Piccadilly Road, Swinton, Near Mexborough. Thursdays, 7 p.m.

Mid-Kent Astronomical Society
Secretary: Brian A. van de Peep, 11 Berber Road, Strood, Rochester, Kent.
Meetings: Medway Teachers Centre, Vicarage Road, Strood, Rochester, Kent. Last Friday in month. Mid Kent College, Horsted. 2nd Friday in month.

Mid-Sussex Astronomical Society
Secretary: Dr L. K. Brundle, 63 Pasture Hill Road, Haywards Heath, West Sussex.
Meetings: Haywards Heath College, Harlands Road, Haywards Heath. Monthly, Wednesdays 7.30 p.m.

Milton Keynes Astronomical Society
Secretary: The Secretary, Milton Keynes Astronomical Society, Bradwell Abbey Field Centre, Bradwell, Milton Keynes MK1 39AP.
Meetings: Alternate Tuesdays.

Moray Astronomical Society
Secretary: Richard Pearce, 1 Forsyth St, Hopeman, Elgin, Moray, Scotland.

Newbury Amateur Astronomical Society
Secretary: Mrs A. Davies, 11 Sedgfield Road, Greenham, Newbury, Berks.
Meetings: United Reform Church Hall, Cromwell Road, Newbury. Last Friday of month, Aug.–May.

Newcastle-on-Tyne Astronomical Society
Secretary: C. E. Willits, 24 Acomb Avenue, Seaton Delaval, Tyne and Wear.
Meetings: Zoology Lecture Theatre, Newcastle University. Monthly.

Newtonian Observatory Astronomical Society
Secretary: Miss P. E. Randle, 62 Northcott Road, Worthing, Sussex.
Meetings: Adult Education Centre, Union Place, Worthing, Sussex. 1st Wednesday each month except Aug. 7.30 p.m.

North Aston Space & Astronomical Club
Secretary: W. R. Chadburn, 14 Oakdale Road, North Aston, Sheffield.
Meetings: To be notified.

Northamptonshire Natural History Astronomical Society
Secretary: Dr Nick Hewitt, 4 Daimler Close, Northampton.
Meetings: Humphrey Rooms, Castillian Terrace, Northampton. 2nd and last Monday each month.

North Devon Astronomical Society
Secretary: P. G. Vickery, 12 Broad Park Crescent, Ilfracombe, North Devon.
Meetings: Pilton Community College, Chaddiford Lane, Barnstaple. 1st Wednesday each month, Sept.–May.

North Dorset Astronomical Society
Secretary: J. E. M. Coward, The Pharmacy, Stalbridge, Dorset.
Meetings: Charterhay, Stourton, Caundle, Dorset. 2nd Wednesday each month.

North Staffordshire Astronomical Society
Secretary: N. Oldham, 25 Linley Grove, Alsager, Stoke-on-Trent.
Meetings: 1st Wednesday of each month at Cartwright House, Broad Street, Hanley.

North Western Association of Variable Star Observers
Secretary: Jeremy Bullivant, 2 Beaminster Road, Heaton Mersey, Stockport, Cheshire.
Meetings: Four annually.
Norwich Astronomical Society
Secretary: Malcolm Jones, Tabor House, Norwich Road, Malbarton, Norwich.
Meetings: The Observatory, Colney Lane, Colney, Norwich. Every Friday, 7.30 p.m.
Nottingham Astronomical Society
Secretary: C. Brennan, 40 Swindon Close, Giltbrook, Nottingham.
Oakham School Observing Society
Secretary: M. A. Nowell, Chapel Close, Oakham School, Oakham, Rutland.
Meetings: As arranged.
Oaktree Astronomy Club
Secretary: Nigel Dickerson, 6c Fern Hill, Dersingham, Norfolk.
Oldham Astronomical Society
Secretary: P. J. Collins, 25 Park Crescent, Chadderton, Oldham.
Meetings: Werneth Park Study Centre, Frederick Street, Oldham. Fortnightly, Friday.
Open University Astronomical Society
Secretary: Jim Lee, c/o above, Milton Keynes.
Meetings: Open University, Walton Hall, Milton Keynes. As arranged.
Orpington Astronomical Society
Secretary: Miss Lucinda Jones, 263 Crescent Drive, Petts Wood, Orpington, Kent.
Meetings: Newstead Wood School or Darrick Wood School, 3rd Thursday each month, Oct.–June, 7.30 p.m.
Oxford & District Astronomical Society
Secretary: Mark Bailey, 52 Burrell Rd, Compton, Newbury, Berkshire.
Plymouth Astronomical Society
Secretary: Sheila Evans, 40 Billington Close, Eggbuckland, Plymouth.
Meetings: Glynnis Kingdon Centre. 2nd Friday each month.
Portsmouth Astronomical Society
Secretary: G. B. Bryant, 81 Ringwood Road, Southsea.
Meetings: Monday. Fortnightly.
Preston & District Astronomical Society
Secretary: P. Sloane, 77 Ribby Road, Wrea Green, Kirkham, Preston, Lancs.
Meetings: Moor Park (Jeremiah Horrocks) Observatory, Preston. 2nd Wednesday. Last Friday each month. 7.30 p.m.
The Pulsar Group
Secretary: Barry Smith, 157 Reridge Road, Blackburn, Lancs.
Meetings: Amateur Astronomy Centre, Clough Bank, Bacup Road, Todmorden, Lancs. 1st Thursday each month.
Rayleigh Astronomical Society
Secretary: Peter Wotherspoon, 103 Grove Road, Rayleigh, Essex.
Meetings: Fitzwimarc School, Hockley Road, Rayleigh. Every Wednesday, 8 p.m.
Reading Astronomical Society
Secretary: Mrs Muriel Wrigley, 516 Wokingham Road, Earley, Reading.
Meetings: St Peter's Church Hall, Church Road, Earley. Monthly (3rd Sat.), 7 p.m.
Renfrew District Astronomical Society (formerly Paisley A.S.)
Secretary: Robert Law, 14d Marmion Court, Forkes, Paisley.
Richmond & Kew Astronomical Society
Secretary: Emil Pallos, 10 Burleigh Place, Cambalt Road, Putney, London SW15.
Meetings: Richmond Central Reference Library, Richmond, Surrey.
Salford Astronomical Society
Secretary: J. A. Handford, 45 Burnside Avenue, Salford 6, Lancs.
Meetings: The Observatory, Chaseley Road, Salford.
Salisbury Plain Astronomical Society
Secretary: R. J. D. Dias.
Scarborough & District Astronomical Society
Secretary: D. M. Mainprize, 76 Trafalgar Square, Scarborough, N. Yorks.
Meetings: Scarborough Public Library. Last Saturday each month, 7–9 p.m.
Scottish Astronomers Group
Secretary: G. Young c/o Mills Observatory, Balgay Park, Ancrum, Dundee.
Meetings: Bi-monthly, around the Country. Syllabus given on request.
Sheffield Astronomical Society
Secretary: Mrs Lilian M. Keen, 21 Seagrave Drive, Gleadless, Sheffield.
Meetings: City Museum, Weston Park, 3rd Friday each month. 7.30 p.m.
Sidmouth and District Astronomical Society
Secretary: M. Grant, Salters Meadow, Sidmouth, Devon.
Meetings: Norman Lockyer Observatory, Salcombe Hill. 1st Monday in each month.

Solent Amateur Astronomers
Secretary: R. Smith, 16 Lincoln Close, Woodley, Romsey, Hants.
Meetings: Room 2, Oaklands Community Centre, Fairisle Road, Lordshill, Southampton. 3rd Tuesday.

Southampton Astronomical Society
Secretary: C. R. Braines, 1a Drummond Road, Hythe, Southampton.
Meetings: Room 148, Murray Building, Southampton University, 2nd Thursday each month, 7.30 p.m.

South Astronomical Society
Secretary: G. T. Elston, 34 Plummer Road, Clapham Park, London SW4 8HH.

South Downs Astronomical Society
Secretary: J. Green, 46 Central Avenue, Bognor Regis, West Sussex.
Meetings: Assembly Rooms, Chichester. 1st Friday in each month.

South East Essex Astronomical Society
Secretary: C. Jones, 92 Long Riding, Basildon, Essex.
Meetings: Lecture Theatre, Central Library, Victoria Avenue, Southend-on-Sea. Generally 1st Thursday in month, Sept.–May.

South-East Kent Astronomical Society
Secretary: P. Andrew, 7 Farncombe Way, Whitfield, nr. Dover.
Meetings: Monthly.

South Lincolnshire Astronomical & Geophysical Society
Secretary: G. T. Walker, 19 Guntons Road, Newborough, Peterborough.
Meetings: South Holland Centre, Spalding. 3rd Thursday each month, 7.30 p.m.

South London Astronomical Society
Chairman: P. Bruce, 2 Constance Road, West Croydon CR0 2RS.
Meetings: Surrey Halls, Birfield Road, Stockwell, London SW4. 2nd Tuesday each month, 8 p.m.

Southport Astronomical Society
Secretary: R. Rawlinson, 188 Haig Ave, Southport, Merseyside.
Meetings: Monthly Sept.–May, plus observing sessions.

Southport, Ormskirk and District Astronomical Society
Secretary: J. T. Harrison, 92 Cottage Lane, Ormskirk, Lancs L39 3NJ.
Meetings: Saturday evenings, monthly as arranged.

South Shields Astronomical Society
Secretary: H. Haysham, Marine and Technical College, St George's Avenue, South Shields.
Meetings: Marine and Technical College. Each Thursday, 7.30 p.m.

South Somerset Astronomical Society
Secretary: G. McNelly, 11 Laxton Close, Taunton, Somerset.
Meetings: Victoria Inn, Skittle Alley, East Reach, Taunton. Last Saturday each month, 7.30 p.m.

South West Cotswolds Astronomical Society
Secretary: C. R. Wiles, Old Castle House, The Triangle, Malmesbury, Wilts.
Meetings: 2nd Friday each month, 8 p.m. (Sept.–June).

South West Herts Astronomical Society
Secretary: Frank Phillips, 54 Highfield Way, Rickmansworth, Herts.
Meetings: Rickmansworth. Last Friday each month, Sept.–May.

Stafford and District Astronomical Society
Secretary: Mrs L. Hodkinson, Beecholme, Francis Green Lane, Penkridge, Staffs.
Meetings: Riverside Centre, Stafford. Every 3rd Thursday, Sept.–May, 7.30 p.m.

Stirling Astronomical Society
Secretary: R. H. Lynn, 25 Pullar Avenue, Bridge of Allan, Stirling.
Meetings: Old Stirling High School, Academy Road, Stirling. Last Tuesday each month, 7.30 p.m.

Stoke-on-Trent Astronomical Society
Secretary: M. Pace, Sundale, Dunnocksfold Road, Alsager, Stoke-on-Trent.
Meetings: Cartwright House, Broad Street, Hanley. Monthly.

Sussex Astronomical Society
Secretary: Mrs C. G. Sutton, 75 Vale Road, Portslade, Sussex.
Meetings: English Language Centre, Third Avenue, Hove. Every Wednesday, 7.30–9.30 p.m. Sept.–May.

Swansea Astronomical Society
Secretary: G. P. Lacey, 32 Glenbran Road, Birchgrove, Swansea.
Meetings: Dillwyn Llewellyn School, John Street, Cockett, Swansea. Second and fourth Thursday each month at 7.30 p.m.

Tavistock Astronomical Society
Secretary: D. S. Gibbs, Lanherne, Chollacott Lane, Whitchurch, Tavistock, Devon.
Meetings: Science Laboratory, Kelly College, Tavistock. 1st Wednesday in month. 7.30 p.m.

Thames Valley Astronomical Group
  Secretary: K. J. Pallet, 82a Tennyson Street, South Lambeth, London SW8 3TH.
  Meetings: Irregular.
Thanet Amateur Astronomical Society
  Secretary: P. F. Jordan, 85 Crescent Road, Ramsgate.
  Meetings: Hilderstone House, Broadstairs, Kent. Monthly.
Todmorden Astronomical Society
  Secretary: Eric Lord, Sloterdisk, 15 Mons Road, Todmorden, Lancashire.
  Meetings: Monthly at Todmorden College.
Torbay Astronomical Society
  Secretary: R. Jones, St Helens, Hermose Road, Teignmouth, Devon.
  Meetings: Town Hall, Torquay. 3rd Thursday, Oct.–May.
Usk Astronomical Society
  Secretary: D. J. T. Thomas, 20 Maryport St., Usk, Gwent.
  Meetings: Usk Adult Education Centre, Maryport St. Weekly, Thursdays (term dates).
Vectis Astronomical Society
  Secretary: J. W. Smith, 27 Forest Road, Winford, Sandown, I.W.
  Meetings: 4th Friday each month, except Dec. at Lord Louis Library Meeting Room, Newport, I.W.
Warwickshire Astronomical Society
  Secretary: R. D. Wood, 20 Humber Road, Coventry, Warwickshire.
  Meetings: 20 Humber Road, Coventry. Each Tuesday.
Webb Society
  Secretary: S. J. Hynes, 8 Cormorant Close, Sydney, Crewe, Cheshire.
  Meetings: As arranged.
Wellingborough District Astronomical Society
  Secretary: S. M. Williams, 120 Brickhill Road, Wellingborough, Northants.
  Meetings: On 2nd Wednesday. Gloucester Hall, Church Street, Wellingborough, 7.30 p.m.
Wessex Astronomical Society
  Secretary: Mrs J. Broadbank, 154a Albert Road, Parkstone, Poole, Dorset BH12 2HA.
  Meetings: The Cafe Lounge, Allendale Centre, Wimborne, Dorset. 1st Tuesday of each month (except August).
West of London Astronomical Society
  Secretary: A. H. Davis, 49 Beaulieu Drive, Pinner, Middx. HA5 1NB.
  Meetings: Monthly, alternately at Hillingdon and North Harrow. 2nd Monday of the month, except August.
West Midland Astronomical Association
  Secretary: Miss S. Bundy, 93 Greenridge Road, Handsworth Wood, Birmingham.
  Meetings: Dr Johnson House, Bull Street, Birmingham. As arranged.
West Yorkshire Astronomical Society
  Secretary: J. A. Roberts, 76 Katrina Grove, Purston, Pontefract, Yorks. WF7 5LW.
  Meetings: The Barn, 4 The Butts, Back Northgate, Pontefract. Every Tuesday, 7 p.m.
Whittington Astronomical Society
  Secretary: P. Klages, 1 Wilfred Owen Avenue, Oswestry, Shropshire.
  Meetings: As arranged.
Wolverhampton Astronomical Society
  Secretary: M. Astley, Garwick, 8 Holme Mill, Fordhouses, Wolverhampton.
  Meetings: Beckminster Methodist Church Hall, Birches Road, Wolverhampton. Alternate Mondays, Sept.–April.
Worcester Astronomical Society
  Secretary: Arthur Wilkinson, 179 Henwick Road, St Johns, Worcester.
  Meetings: Room 117, Worcester College of Higher Education, Henwick Grove, Worcester. 2nd Thursday each month.
Wycombe Astronomical Society
  Secretary: P. A. Hodgins, 50 Copners Drive, Holmer Green, High Wycombe, Bucks.
  Meetings: 3rd Wednesday each month, 7.45 p.m.
York Astronomical Society
  Secretary: Simon Howard, 20 Manor Drive South, Acomb, York.
  Meetings: Goddricke College, York University. 1st and 3rd Fridays.

Any society wishing to be included in this list of local societies or to update details are invited to write to the Editor (c/o Messrs Sidgwick & Jackson (Publishers), Ltd, 1 Tavistock Chambers, Bloomsbury Way, London WC1A 2SG), so that the relevant information may be included in the next edition of the *Yearbook*.